MORE FROM
THE PRIMEVAL FOREST

Religious Books in the Fontana Series

More from the Primeval Forest

ALBERT SCHWEITZER

COLLINS
fontana books

MORE FROM THE PRIMEVAL FOREST
is published by A. & C. Black Limited,
4, 5 & 6 Soho Square, London, W.1.
by arrangement with whom the
Fontana Edition (1958) is published

PRINTED IN GREAT BRITAIN
COLLINS CLEAR-TYPE PRESS: LONDON AND GLASGOW

CONTENTS

PUBLISHERS' NOTE

Just as Dr. Schweitzer's well-known account of the founding of his hospital in French Equatorial Africa, *On the Edge of the Primeval Forest*, was based on letters which he wrote to friends in Europe during his first stay at Lambarene, 1913-1917, so this present volume has its origin in the reports which he sent home during his second period in Africa, 1924-27

His biographer, Dr. George Seaver, regards it as an even finer and more informative narrative, because the product of fuller experience : "it is impossible to do even the faintest justice either to the wealth of interest or to the inspiration of this book, or to measure the immensity of the 'toils and conflicts' against the magnitude of the achievement."

Both the *Primeval Forest* books are published in Fontana.

INTRODUCTION

THE following sketches, which were put together in intervals of leisure during my second period of work at Lambarene between April, 1924, and July, 1927, were not originally meant to appear in book form as a continuation of the volume entitled *On the Edge of the Primeval Forest*, which was published nearly ten years ago, and describes my work in Equatorial Africa during the years 1913-17. They were meant to be just letters for circulation in print among the friends of my undertaking to tell them about what was happening in the hospital. But in compliance with requests from different quarters, I have now decided to let them appear, somewhat shortened, as a book.

Two things unfortunately hindered me from undertaking the labour necessary for this publication during the visit to Europe —from the autumn of 1927 to November, 1929—which followed my second period of activity in Africa: these were first fatigue, and then the necessity of completing as soon as possible the work on the Mysticism of S. Paul, which was begun thirty years ago.

It is only now, when I am again in Lambarene, where I arrived at Christmas, 1929, and again at work, that I can face it. During the first few months here, indeed, the claims of the hospital weighed so heavily on me, that doing anything with a pen was out of the question. Now, however, in the summer of 1930, when I have with me the young Alsatian doctor who came to relieve me of much of the work, and when I am again inured to the climate of the Equatorial forest, I feel fresh enough in the evenings, when the hospital work is over, to devote myself to this different activity.

While I am writing and going again in memory over the activities of which this book is a record, I think with deep emotion of the kind friends in England who by their gifts have helped to make it possible for me to take up the work in Lambarene again and to carry it further. I shall never forget what they have done for me, and I ask them to accept this book as dedicated to them in proof of my gratitude.

7

As with *On the Edge of the Primeval Forest* and the two first volumes of the *Philosophy of Civilisation*, my dear friend, C. T. Campion, is once more exercising for me his skill as a translator. I here offer him my hearty thanks.

A. S.

LAMBARENE
August 8th, 1930

CHAPTER ONE

The Voyage

EARLY on Thursday, February 21st, 1924, while it is still
dark, the Dutch steamer *Orestes* leaves the port of Bordeaux, carrying me to Africa for my second period of work
there. As I have been busy all the night through, writing
important letters so as to be able to get them to post, I go
to bed and sleep till near midday, when I find the boat
leaving the Gironde for the open sea in brilliant sunshine.

At first I can hardly realise that I am returning to Lambarene. The whole time I have lived through since the
shores of the Gironde rose into sight on my return in 1917,
sweeps before my mind's eye, as the same stretch of coast
now gradually disappears. First came the long tale of
months after the war, filled with anxiety about health and
even about life itself, months during which I could make no
plans at all, because it was uncertain whether I should ever
regain the vigour needed for work in the tropics. Then the
year 1920, during which my strength steadily increased,
and I found that I was again fit to do something in science
and in art. After delivering some lectures at the University
of Upsala, in which, during the early summer of that year,
I for the first time broached the ideas contained in my
Philosophy of Civilisation, I ventured, with encouragement
from Archbishop Nathan Söderblom, to give some concerts
and public lectures in Sweden, in order to pay off the heavy
debts still owing on my hospital. This effort was almost too
much for my strength, but the success it met with decided
me to return to Strasbourg with a resolution to resume the
work at Lambarene. When we left Sweden my wife was
ready for the great sacrifice of consenting to my plan,
although owing to the state of her health she would be unable to accompany me. At last I was in a position to pro-

mise what they wanted to the natives who had been bombarding me with entreaties to go out and be their doctor again. But the carrying out of the plan was still in the far distance. For more than two years I had to stay in Europe to give concerts and popular lectures in order to raise funds for the new work, as well as many academic lectures which I had promised to a number of Universities; there was also the task of getting ready for the press the manuscripts of *The Decay and Restoration of Civilisation* and of *Civilisation and Ethics*.

On all these things and on the many weeks devoted to buying and packing the necessary supplies I keep thinking, as the ship leaves the estuary for the open sea, and begins rocking on its waves. I can hardly realise that once more, as in 1913, it is carrying me and all my packing-cases towards the Equator.

Nor is my satisfaction unqualified. My thoughts sweep back to that first start, when my wife, as a loyal helpmeet, was travelling with me. Unceasingly I thank her in my heart that she rose to the sacrifice of acquiescence in my return under these circumstances to Lambarene.

I think, too, of the many dear people whose friendship I won in almost every country in Europe during my lecture and concert tours. Again I feel overpowered by remembrance of the affection I had the privilege of winning from people with whom I could not speak in their own language, but who nevertheless welcomed me as if I were a friend of their own, and helped me to get together what has enabled me to go out to work among the sick and poor of the Ogowe district. What an abundance of friendship I met with in England alone during my two short visits to that country!

My companion on this voyage is an eighteen-year-old Oxford undergraduate, Noel Gillespie, who is ready to spend some months with me in Lambarene, and help me in the heavy work of beginning afresh.

I have purposely chosen to travel by a cargo-boat which will have many stopping-places big and little. I want to get to know the west coast as thoroughly as I can, and I hope to be able to work better than I should be able to on a mail-boat, on which one is continually interrupted by the other passengers. Before we get to Lambarene hundreds of letters must be dealt with, which on account of the pressure of work could not be answered in Europe. At Bordeaux a customs officer spent a whole hour and a half rummaging in trunks filled with these letters, because he could not fathom why anyone should be going off with so many letters addressed to himself! As the export of gold from France was at that time strictly prohibited, he supposed that some at least of the numerous envelopes must contain gold or banknotes, which I was hoping by this ingenious method to smuggle out of the country.

During the voyage we have a splendid north wind behind us.

The ship touches at Dakar, Conakry, Freetown, Sassandra, Grand Lahou, Grand Bassam, Secondee, Accra, Lome, Cotonou, Fernando Po, and Duala.

It has on board as passenger, the only one besides ourselves, a lady who is travelling to the Cameroons. When off Cotonou this passenger takes advantage of the presence of a doctor in the ship to bring into the world a baby which was not expected till she should be at Duala. As there is no other woman on board, the care of her falls on me, and the care of the baby on Noel, who now learns what the temperature of a ship's galley is in the tropics. Eight times a day he has to visit the galley to prepare the milk for the feeding-bottle.

At Duala we leave the ship for a fortnight's expedition in order to visit an, at that time, abandoned station of the Basle mission, named Nyasoso, in the English part of the Cameroons. I wanted to learn about its situation, and the conditions of life in that district, in case I should one day want to start another hospital, an offshoot from Lambarene. This neighbourhood had been recommended to me in several quarters as suitable. So in order to discuss this quite nebulous plan with the Resident, Major Ruxton, we make our way to Buca, which is situated on the slope of the Cameroon Mountain, about 3,200 feet above the sea, and we enjoy there for two days the hospitality of the Resident and his wife. The plan of another hospital in Nyasoso I subsequently for various reasons allowed to drop.

The day after Palm Sunday we leave the Cameroons in the mail-boat *Europe*, the vessel which had brought me to Africa in 1913, and in two days we are in Cape Lopez, or Port Gentil, as it is now called. On the beach I am recognised by natives, who can hardly contain themselves for joy at having " our doctor " back again.

During the afternoon of Maundy Thursday we leave Cape Lopez on board the *Alembe*, on which I went up the Ogowe in 1913. What a dirty old ramshackle boat it has become! But among the white timber-merchants on board I meet several old acquaintances, who give me a hearty welcome.

Through the quietness of Good Friday I travel once more along " the edge of the primeval forest," past the same antediluvian landscape, the same papyrus swamps, the same decaying villages, and the same ragged negroes. How poor this territory is compared with the Gold Coast and the Cameroons! And poor because . . . it is so rich in valuable timber! The exploitation of the forests goes on at the expense of the cultivation of the means of life, and these have to be imported. So wherever we stop we see the same sort of cargo unloaded : sacks of rice, cases of ship's biscuit, cases of dried fish, and, with these, casks of red wine.

At table, as soon as timber-prices and labour have been sufficiently discussed, the conversation turns to the bands of human leopards whose depredations have much increased everywhere in recent years, and have spread over the whole of the west coast. The missionaries at Duala told me how they sometimes visit districts which have been so terrorised by these creatures that no one ventures out of his hut after dark. Two years ago they actually perpetrated a murder at the Lambarene mission station.

They are men who are possessed by the delusion that they are leopards, and therefore must kill men, and when they are out to do this, they try to behave altogether like leopards. They go on all fours, fastening on their hands and feet real leopard's claws or iron imitations of them, so as to leave behind them a spoor like that of a leopard; and when they catch a victim, they sever his carotid artery, as leopards do.

The remarkable and uncanny fact is that most of them have become human leopards involuntarily, having been made members of one of the bands without being aware of it. The band prepares in a human skull a potion made out of the blood of one of their victims, and some man, on whom they have previously fixed, is secretly given some of it in one of his ordinary drinks. Then he is informed that he has drunk the potion, and therefore is from that time one of the band. Nor does any one of them resist. They are all alike, dominated by the belief that a magic potion has some magic power against which no one can successfully fight, and so they obey unresistingly. The next step is a command to take one of their brothers or sisters to some place where he or she can be attacked and killed by the members of the band. Then they must themselves start killing.

An official in the hinterland of the Ogowe district, who a few months before had received orders to put an end to the depredations of the human leopards, captured ninety suspicious characters. They would, however, betray nothing, and poisoned each other in the prisons.

How far these bands of human leopards mean just a wave of pure superstition, and how far they have gone on to adopt the definite objects of revenge and plunder, it is impossible to decide. Like other secret associations they are signs of an uncanny process of fermentation which is going on in the heart of Africa. Reviving superstition, primitive fanaticism, and very modern bolshevism are to-day combining in the strangest way in the Dark Continent.

What a relief it is after conversation about such things to escape to the deck and lose oneself in the contemplation of nature! The boat moves slowly upstream along the dark bank. Wood and water are flooded with the soft light of the

Easter full-moon, and one can hardly bring oneself to believe that under such a flood of light there can be so much misery and terror as we are assured exists.

At sunrise on Easter Eve, April 19th, we are at Lambarene, but it is a long time before we see the canoes from the mission station, which is on one of the side-streams of the Ogowe, and an hour's journey from the steamer's landing-place. Nor are they sufficient to take our numerous packages. Others belonging to natives have to be called for, and volunteer crews obtained. However, we do at last secure transport enough, and get it properly loaded. The paddles dip into the water, and we are soon at the bend where we enter the side-stream and the houses of the mission station on their three small hills become visible. How much I have lived through since in the autumn of 1917 my wife and I lost sight of them! How often have I been on the point of giving up all hope of ever seeing them again! Now, here they are once more; but I no longer have my helpmeet with me. . . .

We get on shore about midday, and while Noel superintends the unloading I walk up to the hospital like one in a dream. It might be the Sleeping Beauty's place of concealment! Grass and brushwood are growing where once stood the wards which I constructed with so much trouble. Above what is still standing are stretched the boughs of big trees which I remember as little saplings. There are still standing, the building of corrugated iron in which we had our operating-room, consulting-room, and dispensary, and another in which we housed some of the patients. These two are still in fairly good condition, though their roofs of palm-leaves are hopelessly damaged.

The path from the hospital up to the little doctor's house on the hill is so overgrown with grass that I can scarcely follow its windings. "To-morrow, the first thing," says Missionary Herrmann, "the boys shall clear it."

"Oh no," is my answer, "let me tread it clear again!"

M. Herrmann and M. Pelot, who are both from Switzerland, Madame Herrmann and the school mistress, Mademoiselle Arnoux, who at the present time form the staff of the mission, are dear acquaintances made during my first period here, and by the time we are seated together at table I feel myself quite at home again in Lambarene.

M. Herrmann and M. Pelot have tried to keep my leaf-roof in a state of repair, but had to abandon the task more than a year ago. There are no more stitched-leaf tiles to be had. In view of two international exhibitions in Europe and America the demand for timber is so great that the Ogowe merchants are quite unable to fulfil the orders that are showered in on them. Anyone who can handle an axe finds well-paid work in the forest. Anyone who knows anything about rafts takes rafts down the river. The few natives who have learnt a trade no longer work at it, since they can earn more in the forest.

Of the carpenters who wrote to me, either themselves or through others, that they were ready to help me with my repairs, not one is near, and no one even knows where they are. Moreover, for months no one has given a thought to stitching raphia leaves over bamboos to make leaf-tiles, except those who have to supply them, as compulsory service to the Government. The natives have not even for themselves any material for roofing their huts; the roofs of their huts are as ruinous as the roofs of our buildings.

All this is bad news, and the state of things is worse than I expected. With holes as big as one's fist in the roofs I cannot put away my belongings or begin work, so there is nothing for it but to find some leaf-tiles as soon as possible and at any price. By three o'clock, therefore, although it is Easter Eve, I am seated in a canoe with Noel to visit a village an hour and a half away where I am well known. There is hand-shaking and an exchange of compliments, and I go from hut to hut, peering about in hopes of finding some stitched-leaf tiles somewhere. An old negro to whom I complain about my pressing need, leads me behind one of the huts, and there are twenty lying on the ground. I make a few more similar discoveries and end with sixty-four!

But the flattery and the presents I had to distribute in order to be able to take the leaf-tiles away with me I should like to forget! I even go so far as to threaten that if the people will not meet my requests, I will never treat any sick person from that village. But such threats, coming from "our Doctor," were only greeted with laughter. To conclude, however—as darkness falls Noel and I return to Lambarene in pouring rain but in possession of sixty-four leaf-tiles!

I can, therefore, keep Easter with a contented mind, for the worst holes can be mended. But how very differently had I pictured to myself the first days after our return! As it is, the prose of Africa has got hold of me, and it will be a long time before it releases its grip.

We can have, at first, only two rooms in the small, doctor's house, the other two being occupied by M. Pelot, and in one of ours a swarm of wild bees has established itself. Some months before, in consequence of a heavy storm, the house had threatened to collapse, as at a height of six feet M. Pelot has protected it with a kind of breastplate of strong oak planks.

For our meals we remain the guests of Madame Herrmann.

CHAPTER II

The First Months in Lambarene

EASTER MONDAY sees our first patients arrive, among them several old people with heart complaints and in very poor condition, for whom scarcely anything can be done. We therefore get many deaths in the first weeks. With one of these bad cases I sat up a whole night hoping to save him by means of injections of caffein, ether, and camphor, with the result that a small native girl in the mission station believes me to be a human leopard. She runs away in terror every time she sees me, and though the schoolmistress tries to talk her out of her fear, it is of no use. " I saw them," she says, " take the man into the hospital in the evening, and he was alive. Then came the doctor and was alone with him the whole night. In the morning they brought him out dead. Evidently the doctor killed him. He is a white human leopard who is allowed to go about freely, while they shut up the black ones in prison."

For our rebuilding operations help comes from a black timber-merchant, Emil Ogouma, who puts at my disposal five labourers and a foreman. These undertake the most urgent repairs, while I look after the sick and unpack the cases of drugs and other things which are still here, left over from my first period of work.

In a fortnight's time we have the dispensary and the consulting-room ready with the absolutely necessary fittings, and then the big ward for the patients is taken in hand. But for that our supply of leaf-tiles is not sufficient, although I have meanwhile secured another 200. And we are still in the rainy season; there are heavy storms every night, and in the morning I find my patients lying on the floor wet through. The result is a number of chills, two of which end fatally. I am quite in despair, and many an afternoon which I wanted urgently for the sick or for get-

ting things straight at home, I spend going about in a
canoe, hunting for leaf-tiles! Many a journey, too, does
Noel make in my stead for the same purpose.

By Ascensiontide the roof of the big ward has been fairly
well repaired, and the building of a second can be taken in
hand. Under the same roof there will be rooms for the
stocking of bottles and tins, for the storage of the washing-
boiler, the building materials, and our stuff generally.
While this work is going on Emil Ogouma's men leave me,
their contract-year being up, and go home, no offer of high
pay being of avail to persuade them into staying for even a
month longer. Their employer will not succeed in recruiting others in their place, and I am making no attempt to do
so. The call for labour is so incessant in the district that I
know it would be useless. I am therefore thrown back upon
volunteers who have come with the patients as their attendants, and have to play myself the part of building-super-
intendent, routing the people out every morning from
behind their cooking-pots, flattering them, promising them
food and presents, forcing the tools into their hands, and in
the evening seeing that all the axes, hatchets, bush-knives,
and all unused material have been brought back.

Sometimes I have half a dozen workers, sometimes a
couple; often when I come down in the morning I cannot
find a single one. They have gone fishing, or have left to
visit their village and get a supply of food, or they had to
go somewhere to take part in a great palaver. Then the
work is at a standstill for days. The zeal of my coloured
folk to provide for those who will come after them better
quarters than they have themselves is very small. They do
not work for those they do not know.

The indifference of primitive man towards persons he
does not know is beyond anything we can conceive. One
day, towards evening, a wounded man had to be brought
hastily from the ward to the consulting-room to have his
dressings renewed. I asked a man who was sitting by the
fire, and whose sick brother I was nursing, to lend a hand
with the stretcher. He pretended not to hear, and on my
repeating the request somewhat more pressingly, he ans-

wered quite calmly : "No. The man on the stretcher is of the Bakele tribe; I am a Bapunu."

Thus I have to divide myself between doctoring and building, the latter being made specially laborious because I have no big canoe. Nor does the mission possess one; it manages with two middle-sized ones, which have had the necessary minimum of repairs. I therefore have great difficulty in getting the bamboos which are to provide the rafters. And time presses. One cannot just go into the forest and cut them; the big bamboos that can be used for this position grow only in certain places in the swamps, and within a radius of many kilometres in this district there is only one place where they are to be found, and from which they can be brought away. For places which lie far away in the swamps, inaccessible either by land or by water, must be left out of account. It is just the same with the raphia palms which provide the materials for the stitched-leaf tiles, and with the plants from the bark of which is made the cord that binds the bamboos to the walls and the leaf-tiles to the bamboos. To get this bark I have to send a canoe something like twenty kilometres.

For the possession of places from which bamboos, raphia, and bark can be easily brought away the tribes used in former days to wage war on each other, just as white nations do for the sake of deposits of metal or coal.

Between Easter and Whitsuntide, when the water reaches its spring high level, I manage with toil and trouble to secure 400 of the 500 bamboo stems which I really need.

About Whitsuntide we get the help of a hospital attendant whom Madame Morel has engaged for us at Samkita. His name is G'Mba; he can read and write well and enjoys the reputation of not being dishonest. He knows nothing at all at present about medicine, although it is a real taste for the work that has made him wish to become an orderly. So I have still to do, with Noel's help, all the work, not being able to entrust to G'Mba even the cleaning of the instruments we use every day.

After Whitsuntide a regular stream of patients begins to come in. The thunderstorms have somewhat abated, and people have learnt that the rain no longer drips through on to the patients.

The number of the sleeping-sickness and leprosy cases that are brought for me to see gives me the impression that these two plagues have been increasing since my last residence here. In Whitsun week I have under treatment as many as twenty-five patients with sleeping-sickness, and about the same number with leprosy. Those with sleeping-sickness I keep here for six weeks; then the treatment stops for eight weeks. They go home and come back again. Unfortunately, I have many cases in the last stage of the disease; they give a great deal of trouble and can hardly ever be saved.

The lepers are sent home at the end of ten days with a supply of Chaulmoogra oil and instructions to come again six weeks later. Intensive treatment with the modern preparations for intramuscular injection I cannot employ till there is more room and I have no longer to be doctor and builder at the same time.

Two-thirds of the hospital inmates are there on account of ulcers. Those caused by syphilis or framboesia I now always treat with intravenous injections of neosalvarsan, which I never had the means of doing before. The treatment requires about a month. I am also trying new preparations of bismuth, and, as it seems to me, with good results.

For children with framboesia, who are often covered all over with sores, I do not as a rule rely on the intravenous injections of salvarsan. I have no need to subject them, with their tiny arm-veins, to this often long and tedious torment. The new drug called stovarsol saves me from that. It is given in the form of easily swallowed pastilles. In four days the scabs over the sores begin to dry up; in eight or ten they fall off, and the child is permanently cured of the disease. Unfortunately this drug is very expensive.

I allow the rumour to spread everywhere that my principle is to give stovarsol only in return for stitched raphia leaves, though I am unable to enforce the restriction. Many a poor mother is not in a position to obtain stitched leaves with which to secure from the doctor the treatment of her child. Still, I have been able, thanks to stovarsol, to get some square yards of roof covered. Chaulmoogra oil, too, it is my principle to give only in return for stitched leaves or bananas, at least to the people in the neighbourhood. Those who come from a distance cannot load their canoes with such things. They must be thankful if they are able to bring with them their sleeping mats, their cooking-pot, their supply of food, and whatever else they will need for the journey, or while they are camping at the hospital.

On the whole, the patients and their companions are really grateful, especially the lepers, those with heart complaints, those whose ulcers have been treated with neosalvarsan, and those who came on account of accidents or wounds. Only I must not be too eager to get tangible proofs of gratitude. If the son of a convalescent father is to help for four or five days at our building or other efforts at improvement, or even to go into the forest to fetch timber, I must encourage his impulse to gratitude with a few presents to prevent its disappearing like an expiring lamp-flame.

The chief of a little village in the Samkita district is with me just now for treatment of a damaged hand, the result of the bursting of the gun with which he was trying to shoot a wild pig. This kind of accident happens much more frequently now than it used to. Down to ten years ago they used to sell to the natives flint-lock muskets which had come down from the military stores of the good old times. Now that these honestly made weapons are sold out, there come to Africa similar muskets of the worst possible make, the barrels of which have more lead than steel in their composition. These treacherous weapons are used with the same heavy charges that were safe with the old style. And a black sportsman, let me add, thinks he can never cram enough powder into the barrel. Moreover, he likes best to use as bullets fragments of cast-iron cooking-pots. Such charges as that are too much for the modern factory musket; hence the many injuries caused by bursting guns.

My little chief, for all the gratitude he feels towards us,

takes care to let Noel and me feel from the very first day that he is a chief, while we are only ordinary mortals. When I begin to bandage him only once a day instead of examining his wound both morning and evening, I must humbly explain to him the reason for it. His authority, however, is not far-reaching enough to bring his relatives, who spend the whole day in the hospital, to show their gratitude by doing a little public work for us. To get from him 150 stitched leaves I have to threaten to stop dressing his hand and to let it " go bad," and as no danger is involved I do, in fact, carry out my threat by not looking at his hand for three or four days. Of the 500 of which I got a promise if his hand got healed, I have as yet seen nothing. But, nevertheless, I think kindly of him. He is in his own way a fine man. There are many things about which one must not argue with a primitive.

That the sufferers from sleeping-sickness and ulcers have to be treated with intravenous injections means a vast amount of work. There are often twenty such injections to be made in one day, and to make them for black people is much more difficult than to make them for white. There is no such bluish tint as shows through the skin of the latter the position of the veins. Moreover, in many cases scratches and cutaneous eruptions have turned our patients' skins into a coat of mail through which the most practised finger can no longer find any blood vessel. Many sleeping-sickness victims, too, are mere skeletons whose miserable little veins make intravenous injections terribly difficult. Repeated trials are therefore often necessary before the needle can find the right way for itself. These difficult cases, a single one of which may sometimes demand an hour's work, are always left to take their turn when the " good veins " have been dealt with. One little girl with sleeping-sickness, Zitombo by name, is the patient we most dread. Many a lump of sugar must be put into her mouth to stop her tears while the needle goes again and again into her poor little arm in search of the vein. And when it is all over, she is carried out of the hospital on the doctor's arm. Saturday is the great day for sleeping-sickness injections, and on that day Madame Herrmann knows that we shall be an hour or two late at meals. But she is very forbearing with us.

Luckily, Noel has acquired very quickly the technique of intravenous injections, so he is able to spare me much work.

Among the natives Noel is known as "the lieutenant." Ever since the military administration of the colony began, it has been the rule to have an official called a lieutenant, in addition to the district captain, and as the people have known army surgeons only, I too have in their eyes something of a military character. Thus it comes easily to them to regard my white colleague as the doctor's lieutenant. Noel has become quite accustomed to the soubriquet, and no one calls him anything else at the mission station.

The praiseworthy habit of dumping sick persons at my hospital and then making themselves scarce has not been lost by the Ogowe people. I have been here barely a fortnight when I find lying in front of it an old man with heart disease, almost naked, and without either blanket or mosquito net, no one knowing how he got there. He himself claims to have a large number of influential relations near Samkita, some of whom will very soon be coming to bring a good supply of food for him and a handsome present for me. I give him a blanket and a mosquito net and some food, and he is with us for several weeks until death releases him. Even when he can hardly speak he continues to refer to his rich relations who will certainly come, and the last service I can do for him in life is to listen to his assurances as if I believed them! The patient next him, who was deposited here in just the same way, is waiting for his death in order to have the use of his mosquito net and blanket, for the supply of these which came with my personal baggage is exhausted, and the seventy-three cases which were sent off from Strasbourg, in February, are still undelivered.

A woman, too, from a village not far from Lambarene, as ragged and as near death as the men, has been deposited here. She has no one at all belonging to her, so no one in the village troubles about her. A neighbour's wife, so I am told, asked another woman to lend her an axe that she might get a little firewood for the old woman to keep her warm during the damp nights. "What?" was the answer. "An axe for that old woman? Take her to the doctor, and leave her there till she dies." And that was what happened.

The prospect of people getting accustomed to depositing here sick or old neighbours whom they want to get rid of is a dangerous one, for it means a heavy burden on the hospital, such persons being sometimes on our hands for months. It means also a great increase in our death-rate, and this depresses the other inmates, especially as the deaths take place before their eyes. For I have not yet got any separate room for hopeless cases.

With the medicine-men, my native colleagues, it never happens that a patient dies. They reject hopeless cases at once, acting in this respect like many doctors in European hospitals, who do not want to have their statistics spoilt. And if a medicine-man does unexpectedly lose a patient, he protects his reputation by finding out at once who bewitched the dead man so that he could not escape dying. The view of the natives is that the very first proof of medical skill is for the doctor to know whether his patient will die or not, so that he may not waste his skill on one who, to speak accurately, is already dead. If he does treat one who afterwards dies, that only proves that he does not even know whether the illness will be fatal or can be cured. Even during my first stay here Joseph was always urging me to get rid of the obviously doomed so as not to damage my reputation. And the same question is still facing us to-day.

Three such foundlings have recently died one after another, and there was grumbling in the hospital. One man with a phagedenic ulcer, on whom I had spent much time and trouble, had himself fetched home by his relations, and two others followed his example. It is not the first time that I have had this experience, but I do not let it modify my ideas. My hospital is open to all sufferers. Even if I cannot save them from death I can at least show them love, and perhaps make their end easier. They are wel-

come, therefore, to come at night and lay such poor creatures at my door. If I succeed in bringing one of them
through, I have no need to trouble about how I am to get
him home. The news that he is capable of working and
therefore can be made use of again, will reach his village
at once, and any night they may come and fetch him away
as secretly as they brought him.

At the grave of the poor woman for whom they would
not provide even a little firewood, M. Herrmann spoke in
touching words of how she was cast off by her own people,
but met with tenderness among strangers, because through
Jesus love had come into the world. And beautiful was the
sunlight as it streamed through the palm trees upon the
poor grave, while the school children sang a funeral hymn.

A burial gives us a great deal of trouble. The procedure
is not so easy as putting a pick or a spade into the hands of
three or four of those who have come here with the patient,
promising them a present, and getting them to dig the
grave. If there is a death, every man who can use a spade
has generally disappeared, ostensibly to fish, or to go home
to fetch food. The native will have nothing to do with a
dead stranger, and primitive religious ideas about " un-
cleanness " play their part in producing this refusal. If, for
example, a birth is expected in a family, no member of it
may have anything to do with a corpse. Often, too, the
parents have vowed at the birth of a child that it shall
never come into contact with a corpse, and this vow it must
observe.

Once I succeeded in concealing the fact of a death
during the night, and so surprising, with the request that
they would dig a grave, two young men whose ulcers were
well on the way to healing that they could not escape. But
when I put the tools into their hands with the promise of a
handsome present, they knelt before me with tears in their
eyes, and besought me not to compel them to do what they
ought not to do. And I could not bring myself to compel
them. In the Epistle to the Romans (Chapter XIV.) S.
Paul orders us to respect weak consciences, and the command holds good to-day in Africa as well as elsewhere. The

Catholic mission has the same difficulty to contend with. A native woman belonging to Catholic circles once died with us, on which I informed the Father Superior, and asked whether he would bury her in the Catholic cemetery. "Yes," he replied, " if people come to dig a grave for her. We have had to give up expecting this work to be done by our schoolboys."

Our digging is generally done by those who are being trained at the mission station to be evangelists; but when they are not at hand, we have to do it ourselves. Noel has often officiated as sexton and bearer. That G'Mba in these cases rises above all prejudices and gives valuable help, I reckon as very much to his credit.

The midday hour is the worst of the whole day, for then every creature who can crawl comes to the consulting-room and asks for a "ration." This food-ration consists of about 600 grammes (c. 21 oz.) of rice with some salt, or seven to ten big bananas, or three to six sticks of manioc. For fat we distribute palm-oil, or, if that is not to be had, tinned vegetable fat imported from Europe. Sometimes there is dried fish, either carp from the Ogowe, which, after the big fishing expeditions in the dry season, is dried over big fires and stored in sacks, or sea-fish from the coast waters of Angola. The patients do their own cooking.

My principle is to give the ration only to those who have come a long distance, or are really poor and have to stay here a considerable time, though I give it also to those who have been working for me on that particular day. These, however, receive at midday only half the ration; the rest they get in the evening, for if they got it at noon they might refuse to do any more work.

But every day there are cases which invite me to abandon my principle, and give rations which were not foreseen as needed. A man who was working for me the previous day is unwell to-day, but hopes to work again to-morrow; he therefore demands a ration to-day. Or sick people who have hitherto received bananas and manioc from their villages come up because for two days none have arrived.

The people at home have perhaps no canoe at their disposal, they say; or they cannot beat up a crew; or the men in the canoe have been taken up by black soldiers because they have not paid their taxes for the gear; or wild pigs have devastated the plantation. . . . I am worked upon with a score of such possible explanations of the stoppage of supplies, till at last I yield, and instruct G'Mba, who is standing behind the rice-trough, to put the petitioners on the list of those to be fed till further notice. But how often the result is that their names are there permanently! If the people in the village get to know that I do not let their relatives starve because their supply of food is delayed, their zeal for supplying it cools down very considerably.

Here is another case. A patient arrives who has some money and with his attendants receives his daily rations from me in return for a reasonable payment. The village is much too far away for supplies to be brought to him, or it is perhaps in a famine district. The illness is protracted, and his money gives out, so he stands in the crowd at midday and begs to be fed with them till further notice. His condition is not such that I can send him away. So what am I to do? I have to feed him and his, and screw myself up to the belief that he will some day make good his promise to reimburse me for my expenditure.

How often, on hearing the Strasbourg cathedral clock strike midday, have I said to myself, " This is just the time when, in Africa, you'll have the palaver about rations, and be lucky if it does not last more than an hour."

Still, I must not be too strict with the petitioners. Not long ago I began to treat with narcotics a man who was getting his food from home, and when I asked him whether he had obeyed my instructions for such cases, not to eat anything in the morning before treatment, he replied : " I've had nothing at all to eat for two days." Because I always show myself so incredulous of the reasons given for the non-arrival of food supplies, he and his wife had not ventured to say anything about their hunger. Of course they were at once put on the list of recipients.

When I am unable to get away from other work, G'Mba

distributes the rations and decides with Solomon-like wisdom whether to give ear to new entreaties or not. And he is much harder than I am. The fact that, driven by necessity, I am compelled to leave the control of it all to him is a great temptation. I can only hope that he does not succumb to it.

The usual number of rations given out daily is between twenty and thirty, though it is often larger. What a number of sacks of rice we have already got through!

Directly after Whitsuntide we have to stop for a time the rebuilding of the second sick-ward, and work with all haste at a strong cell for the mental cases. One of the sleeping-sickness patients, a young woodcutter, N'Gonde by name, has what is often incidental to that disease, viz., fits of excitement, and becomes dangerous. Half a dozen planks are all that I have available. These are nailed to posts fixed in the ground and form the framework of the cell. The spaces between are filled with lengths of hard wood in the round, as thick as one's arm, which are nailed to the planks. The constructor of this provisional cell is Noel, and for more than ten days the posts and N'Gonde together make his life a misery; the former because they are of magnificent African hardwood, so hard that the nails always bend while being hammered into it, and the latter because he always manages to find the weak spots in Noel's work and to break out either at dinner-time or during the night. To enable Noel to work, I have to keep the patient quiet for hours together with scopolamia and morphia. We have no place in which to put him except the cell under construction, for all the living-rooms in the hospital are, of course, constructed just of bamboos and stitched-leaf tiles.

Scarcely is the cell finished, when the floor of our rotten fowl-house falls in under Noel's weight as he is counting the fowls one evening, and that brings about a sympathetic collapse of the walls. Repairs are out of the question, for no nail would hold in the rotten wood, so all other work has to be abandoned and a new fowl-house built as quickly as possible—yes, as quickly as possible, because the old one affords not the slightest protection against snakes or leopards.

Meanwhile, I have discovered, very fortunately, that the husband of a sleeping-sickness patient knows something about carpentry. As his wife is improving, Monenzalie—that is his name—agrees to work regularly for me in return for food and presents.

At last, on June 21st, the steamer brings my seventy-three packing-cases. On the same day there arrives a strong motor-boat for the mission station, and with it a new twenty-three-year-old missionary, M. Abrezol, from Switzerland. He has learnt in Europe how to manage a motor-boat, and at once places himself and the boat at our disposal for towing the canoes which must bring my cases from the steamer's landing-place. There they must be on the grass in the open, exposed to rain and thieves unless we succeed in bringing them over before nightfall. The Catholic mission lends us a big canoe which can take my eight biggest cases at once, and the motor-boat makes it possible for the canoes to make two journeys in the afternoon. Finally, about sundown, there actually arrives by chance a small steamer belonging to a Dutch timber-merchant, who has been under my care for weeks. Of course, his steamer is requisitioned for help with the transport, and by 8 o'clock all the cases, except that containing the cooking stove, are lodged in the open canoe-shed. There they will have to stay for two or three weeks protected from rain so far as the holes in the roof allow, and from thieves so far as is ensured by the wakefulness of the two patients whom I install there as watchmen.

Meanwhile the departure of M. Pelot leaves the doctor's house free, and we can now use all its four rooms. The most urgent repairs are hastily effected, and then the cases are unpacked. We have no cupboards yet, but they are to be provided from the big cases, which have been specially made so that they can be fitted with handles and fixed one upon the other. This work can only be done bit by bit, but the cases must be unpacked at once; the open canoe-shed is a very dangerous place for them. So we can do nothing but pile their contents higgledy-piggledy in the corners of the rooms; linen and kitchen apparatus, surgical instruments and curtains, boots and medicine bottles, books and bandages. To find any particular thing needed, we have to excavate, and tunnel into the piles, like those who want to desecrate the royal tombs in Egypt. This nomadic misery is slightly more tolerable because, having foreseen it while in Strasbourg, I got friendly hands to sew together by the dozen sacks of different sizes, into each of which, as we unpack, we can stuff things of the same category.

From our third week here onwards we have always had two or three white patients, room for them being provided by Noel taking up his quarters on the veranda.

On July 18th we welcome Mademoiselle Mathilde Kottmann from Strasbourg as nurse. Now the clouds are beginning to lift. Never again will our white patients find their beds made with tablecloths instead of sheets. Noel will no longer be responsible for the filling of the lamps, the boiling of the drinking water, or for getting the weekly washing done. Nor will he, in future, have to go in the evening and count the fowls, or conduct a search for possible eggs. I myself shall be relieved of the superintendence of the kitchen and all that is in it. And the piles of goods into which we had to tunnel are disappearing, if slowly, into the cupboards that we have made out of piled-up packing-cases.

At first, indeed, Mademoiselle Kottmann had for weeks so much to do in the house, and in looking after the white patients, that she hardly counted for anything in the hospital. For that, Joseph has at last come back and taken up his work again. How long he will stay I do not know. The timber-trading fever has attacked him too, and he and a few friends have rented a big area of forest which they mean to exploit with workmen engaged for a year. I have to promise that he can absent himself at any time to look after his business. At first his wife takes his place as foreman at the timber-site, which is three days' journey from here. But I am afraid that Joseph, like so many natives who engage in the timber-trade on their own account, will lose money instead of making it.

It gives me great pleasure that some of the few native timber-merchants who have been fairly successful, mean to give me, at the suggestion of Emil Ogouma, some considerable donations for the upkeep of the hospital. They wish to contribute as nearly as they can the cost of Mlle Kottmann's voyage, but I am not sure that such a sum will be collected.

For a good many weeks after Whitsuntide I feel unwell. I have to drag myself to work and I am scarcely back from the hospital at midday and in the evening when I have to lie down. I cannot even manage to make out the order for the necessary drugs and dressings. It is the roof of the hospital that is chiefly to blame for this. I had not noticed that it showed again a number of holes, and I no doubt got several slight sunstrokes. A roof of stitched leaves should really be examined every day. The slightest blast of wind is enough to push the rotten leaves up against one another in such a way that another hole is made.

At the end of May the dry season begins here, and it lasts to the middle of September. This year, however, it does not begin at all. Rainstorms come continually one after another.

That there should be no dry season is something that the natives have never experienced or heard the old people talk of. This gives a shock to many Christians, because, since the native languages have no words for summer and winter, the missionaries have translated the promise of God in Genesis, made after the Flood : "While the earth remaineth, wet season and dry season, day and night, shall never cease." So now they want to be told why it is that the weather does not go on as the Bible says it will.

In July we are greatly upset by the death of the latest missionary recruit, M. Abrezol. Although an exceptionally good swimmer, he was drowned while bathing at dawn in a lake near N'Gômô, before the eyes of M. Herrmann and Noel, with whom he was on a journey.* His body was found, but could not be brought to Lambarene, since the motor-boat had been damaged by grounding on a sand-bank. So he was buried on the hill at N'Gômô. He was a lovable and extraordinarily good all-round man and had won all hearts.

At the beginning of August M. and Madame Morel came to us for a fortnight in order to start for Alsace from here. They have to take the river-steamer here, since it is un-certain whether, with the lower water-level, it will be able to go up as far as Samkita.

M. Morel had not long before killed a boa-constrictor near the girls' school. As it was shot with my gun, I got, as was fitting, half of it for the hospital. Unfortunately, it was only five and a half feet long, and not very fat. The patients very nearly came to blows over the distribution of this dainty.

In the third week of August Noel left us, at the same time as M. Morel. I do not know how to thank sufficiently this good comrade for all the help he gave me. His type-writer, which he used like a practised typist, will be sorely missed by my poor tired hand. But he himself, amid his lectures at Oxford, will remember, as if it were a dream, how once he was in Africa doctor's assistant, carpenter, foreman, sexton, and other things besides.

The doctor's house is never without a white patient as an inmate, and some of these remain for several weeks. Just after Noel's departure four came in about the same time. Those of them who come fresh from several months of camp life at a timber-site, can hardly realise at first that they are now lying in a proper, clean bed. The wife of one of them, who had been sharing the loneliness of the forest with her husband, had first of all to get accustomed to see-ing several white people together.

Now at last I have my permanent cook, viz., Aloys, who was in my service during my first period here. He is quite

* Since then several people have been drowned in the same body of water, or similar ones, in a quite unaccountable way, and we assume that they were paralysed by being stung by an electric fish.

clever, under Mlle Kottmann's direction, at providing from very limited resources attractive and well-varied diet for the patients. One of them had had for several weeks, during a severe attack of fever, nothing to eat but tinned foods, which he was not even able to warm.

The white patients belong to all nationalities. In my little Visitor's Book there are names of English, Swiss, Dutch, Swedish, Canadian, and American patients. Most of them come because of ulcers on the feet or malaria, but I have had two cases of blackwater fever, one of them serious, the other at a very early stage of it. Blackwater fever is a sequela of malaria, producing, under conditions which are not yet understood, a general destruction of the red blood-corpuscles. The resulting debris blocks the kidneys and thus endangers life. The red pigment set free by the destruction of the corpuscles appears in the urine and gives it a dark red colour; hence the name of the disease. The treatment has for its object the arrest of this process of destruction, and this is best attained by eight-hourly injections of half a litre (about $\frac{3}{4}$ pint) of a sterilised 3 per cent solution of common salt. This is very painful, but effective, and, if begun fairly early in the course of the disease, usually saves the patient. One gives at the same time a subcutaneous injection of 20 c.c. of serum. We use for this the anti-snake-bite serum of the Pasteur Institute, which we always keep in stock.

I am having a great deal of trouble with a Canadian who came with numerous deep-seated muscle abscesses. No sooner was one opened than another showed itself. Up to now my lancet has operated on eight. How long the patient can hold out under the discharges of pus, and the constant accompanying fever, weakened as he is by five years in the tropics and exhausting work on timber-sites, I cannot predict.

Such abscesses, which are always multiple, are common here, with whites and blacks alike. The latter, however, never suffer from blackwater fever.

A sailor, who wanted to try his luck at timber-dealing as well, was recently brought to me suffering, after only a few weeks in the district, from pneumonia, and already with the death-rattle in his throat. He died almost immediately, and I found the words, "No luck," tattooed on his chest.

Just at present we have to call up daily at bandaging-time "the leopard man." This is a quiet young fellow who was attacked by a leopard while asleep in his hut. The animal seized his right arm with its paw, but released him on people hurrying up with a light. As the natives know by experience what terrible infection is caused by a leopard's claws, they put the man into a canoe at once to bring him to me. On his arrival twelve hours later the arm was already swollen and hard to the touch, and extremely painful. Fever had set in too. In the skin itself no sign of injury could be seen except four tiny marks which might have been made with a needle. But when the place was opened with a lancet it could be seen that the claws had torn the flesh right down to the bone. Our leopard man will very soon be fit to return home, and meanwhile he makes himself useful by helping to iron the linen.

N'Gonde, too, the sleeping-sickness patient for whom the isolation-cell had to be built, is cured. As he has neither home nor relatives, he will remain in service here as general factotum. His chief task will be roof-mending, at which he is an expert. No sooner was he really better than he said to me : "Now that you have cured me, buy me a wife." That was a job at which I did not jump, but he now has a money-box for savings towards the purchase of a wife. Since becoming roof-mender, he has renounced the name of N'Gonde, and calls himself Ambrosius.

Madame Herrmann and Mlle Arnoux are kind enough to hold a short service every evening about sunset in among the smoky fires and the seething cooking-pots, and the conversation about the Bible passages read out is often lengthy. On one occasion a native, and one of the real savages, too, took Mlle Arnoux to task because she read out that no one had ever seen God. That, he said, was untrue; he himself had once caught sight of God in the forest.

The rainstorms continue, and it is a great misfortune for the country. From May to August is the period when vegetation should be cut down and burnt so that fresh land, manured with wood-ash, may be used for banana plantations. But since this year it is always raining, the people have no heart for cutting down anything, for it will never get dry enough to burn. So we shall have to face a year of famine.

Moreover, since the water keeps at a high level, the natives cannot make any big fishing expeditions, and there are nowhere to be found those supplies of smoked fish which, as a rule, satisfy for months in the year the demand for flesh-food. The Catholic mission, which usually has a good supply of everything, has only about 500 small carp in store for their children. The Father Superior, therefore, who is an excellent shot, goes out hippo-hunting with twelve boys, a whole day's journey away. That means that they must pass the night on a sandbank, or in a swamp in the rain. Then they will return two or three weeks later, perhaps empty-handed, perhaps with the canoe full of smoked hippopotamus flesh, and the latter means that the school work will go on satisfactorily all through the winter. A negro boy who gets meat to eat two or three times a week is willing and eager to learn; without meat he is a listless creature who, even if he is well stuffed with rice, is always complaining of being hungry. The inhabitants of the primeval forest have an almost diseased hunger for flesh-meat.

And now I cannot help fearing that my narrative has given my readers far too much of the prose of Africa, but whatever one gets drowned in fills the mouth. Our life is so filled with this prose that I cannot but write about it. Anyone who wants to do good under our African conditions must fight any tendency in himself to let his nerves and temper be upset by all the big and little difficulties of daily life, and must retain his full joy in his work. So it is all to the good that our far-away friends should experience with us something of the prose of Africa. They are thus in a position to estimate what good it does us here to receive proofs of their affection.

CHAPTER III

Late Autumn to Christmas, 1924

EARLIER than I had ventured to hope has come the fulfilment of my dream of having a doctor to help me. On October 19th, a countryman of my own, Victor Nessmann, began work here. He is the son of a pastor in Alsace, who, when qualifying for the profession, was my fellow-student in Strasbourg.

And his help came in the very nick of time. Not a day longer could I have supported the double burden of builder and doctor. How I had suffered from being unable to make my examinations of patients as thorough as they should have been, because in spite of all my efforts I could not summon sufficient energy for the task! And how it had disquieted me that with the strong and risky remedies that so many tropical diseases demand, I could not give sufficient time to each patient! How often ought microscope and test-tube to have been called upon for guidance and were not! In surgery, too, only the necessary minimum was undertaken.

So the hoot of the river-steamer which is bringing my countryman, means my release from the distress of medical work which, in spite of the best goodwill has to be too superficial. The canoes are quickly manned, and very soon, amid the gently falling rain of the just-beginning wet season, we lie to at the side of the steamer, and my young countryman, who does not know yet what fatigue is, signals to me from the deck. " Now you shall rest, and I will take over all the work " are his words when we shake hands. " Good," I answer; " then begin at once, and look after the loading of the canoes with your trunks and cases." Here is already a test of fitness for life in Africa. Piled on the deck in fine disorder are the trunks and cases. Each passenger has to collect his own from the various heaps and see that his men leave none behind; also that they carry off nothing belonging to someone else, that they let nothing fall into the river, and that they distribute the weight properly in the canoes. The new doctor, who is regarded with astonishment by the natives on account of his youthful appearance, shows himself to be a skilful stevedore. During the passage to shore I can hardly get a word out, so overcome do I feel by the fact that I now have a professional colleague. It is blissful to be able to confess to myself how tired I am.

What was indicated in the transport job is confirmed again and again in the next few days; the new doctor seems to have been made for Africa! He is of a practical turn of mind, has the gift of organisation, and knows how to tackle the natives. Moreover, he has a sense of humour, without which no one can get on properly out here. In spite of his well-developed body, he is called by the natives " the little doctor "—" little " meaning in the language of this district " young."

He is soon quite accustomed to our medical routine, though during the first few weeks he does occasionally betray himself as a newcomer. Having, for example, with much trouble spelt out the quite impossible name of a quite raw native for entry in the register of patients, he goes on, unconsciously following the practice in Europe, to ask for his Christian name!

About the middle of November we lose, through death, our loyal second orderly, G'Mba. Having with leave of absence spent All Saints' Day and All Souls' Day (November 1st and 2nd) with relatives, he returned through heavy rain, and caught cold. Fever supervened, and with all our drugs we could not master it. He himself was quite aware of the seriousness of his condition. By the end of the second week the fever had quite broken down his power of resistance, and his last days were passed in a state of coma. The anxious beseeching looks which he directed at us whenever we were treating him I can never forget, and his death affected us all deeply.

G'Mba was born to be a hospital orderly, and he loved his work, only we could never get him to recognise that care for order and cleanliness in the hospital was one of his duties. He would look on unperturbed while the patients' wives threw their slops and kitchen-refuse on the ground in front of the wards instead of taking them to the rubbish-heap. On one occasion when, not for the first time, I called him to account for this, he answered : " Well, what am I to say to them? My own wife doesn't obey me. How can I expect the other women to listen to me?"

Joseph, too, does not like having anything to do with the non-medical side of the hospital work, because it means having to argue with the sick and their relatives; nor can I feel really annoyed with him. It is very difficult here for any native, whatever his position, to secure obedience from his fellows. At the timber-camps the work is made very much harder because it is impossible to find any black fore-men who can exert authority. The new doctor and I have, therefore, to undertake the duty of supervision in the hospital and everywhere else, and waste far too much time in argumentations big and little instead of being able to leave such things to our staff. So it may happen that the new doctor, who relieves me as much as he can in this matter, has to spend a couple of hours trying to discover which woman it was who threw the kitchen-refuse into the path. As examining-magistrate also he is showing himself to be first-class !

G'Mba's place is taken by Dominic, one of our convales-cents, and he shows himself to be fairly adaptable, though unfortunately he can neither read nor write.

It means a great lightening of our work that Joseph has mastered fairly well the technique of intravenous injections, which play such an important part in the treatment of tropical diseases. With a sufficient amount of supervision, this work can be left almost entirely to him, and it often takes up a whole morning.

The presence of the new doctor allows me to give, if nec-essary, almost the whole day to the building work. The first thing to be done is to provide the two completed buildings with beds, for hitherto I have had enough to do in making and mending roofs. When I say beds, of course I do not use the word in the European sense.

I myself put the frames together with the help of Minkoë, a seventeen-year-old native, whom Madame Morel sent to me from Samkita at the beginning of the summer in pitiable condition with a huge ulcer on one of his feet. Having been cured with neosalvarsan he makes himself as useful as he can. Towards evening the new doctor generally comes to join me, so as to get some change and relief from his medical work by handling hammer and saw.

I want to fit up my hospital with bed-frames of hard-wood, which will rest upon posts in the ground, but can be lifted from the posts and taken out into the sun to be cleaned. In order to make full use of the space protected by the roofs, I put a second tier of beds above the first, as one finds in railway sleeping-cars. The inner part consists of a layer of strips of hardwood of uniform thickness, over which thin bamboos are bound with small vine stems.

Quite the simplest way of making the bed would be to use planks, but I have none available nor any prospect of securing a sufficient number in the near future. I have, therefore, to make them with hardwood strips and bam-boos, which works out more expensively than the dearest planks would be and costs me far more toil. What a number of days have to be spent in collecting the materials! What a number of presents and rations I have to distribute to the people who, under the leadership of Minkoë, under-take the many necessary journeys into the forest and the swamps!

At last about forty beds are ready. Next there is needed a hut which can be locked, for the storage of paddles and tools. There is urgent need, too, for a room where we can store bananas and sacks of rice, and for a big chest with partitions for the sorting and piling together of the tins and big and little bottles in which we give the patients their medicines. How easy everything would be if we had planks! How complicated and troublesome it is if one has to work with wood in the round, especially if it has to be fetched from a distance! And what a task it is to build with such material something which will be safe against thieves!

Often the work ceases for a whole day because the men refuse to go off into the forest. They want first to have a thorough rest from their last expedition. Or it is raining, and then no one can get the natives of Equatorial Africa to work. A day of rain they take as a God-given day of rest. Still, in this objection to getting wet they are not far wrong. Since all natives here are more or less infected with malaria germs, the slightest chill may start an attack of fever, and I myself always take care to give them as little as possible to do in rainy weather.

When these store-rooms are ready, another ward is taken in hand, calculated to hold thirty beds, for the number of our patients is always growing. Every evening now it falls to us to offer shelter to sixty or seventy sick folk without counting those who accompany them. We must also, some day, have a special room with fifteen beds for those who have undergone an operation. If we ever get to practising surgery to the extent that is called for here, it will no longer do for the subjects to be placed among the other sick, just where there happens to be room.

While I give up a great part of my time to these various works, Monenzalie, the carpenter who came here with his wife suffering from sleeping-sickness, is busy constructing a small house of three rooms. It will be built on piles, with a floor of planks and the usual roof of leaf-tiles, and will be for the new doctor and the white patients. To its construction are devoted all the beams and planks I can get hold of. In answer to pressing entreaties I get some old beams offered to me from various quarters. Planks are sawn for me from time to time in small quantities at the saw-pit of the mission at N'Gomo, but then there is the task of getting the wood here. They have to be brought more than twenty-five miles upstream, and some of the beams that have been given me nearly sixty-five miles. Moreover, navigation may be made more difficult by a period of flood. Too often, then, the work on the house for the new doctor and the white patients comes to a stop because there are neither beams nor planks at hand. It is often interrupted, too, because the black carpenter must give all his time to his wife, who is already quite helpless. And he looks after her with touching patience.

He does his work fairly well, but cannot use the footrule properly, because he has never put himself on familiar terms with printed figures. If I tell him that one door must be four inches wider than the rest, he looks at me with embarrassment, and asks me to show him on the footrule how much that is. Consequently, I have to visit the work frequently, give him the measurements, and see that he keeps to them. All the problems, too, which arise from the differences in length and thickness between the beams which our begging has collected require my presence.

Till the new house is ready the young doctor lives in the roomy dwelling of the missionary, M. Herrmann. There the white patients also receive kind hospitality, if there is no room in my house.

The stream of black patients that comes to us now is much stronger than it was during my first residence here, but they are people of a quite different class, and I have regretfully to confess that my hospital is no longer what it was then. This is the result of economic changes in the Ogowe district.

When I was here before, the people who sought my help belonged with few exceptions to the settled population of the country. To-day a large proportion of my patients are savages who have moved hither from the interior, and now work in groups, fifty to a hundred together, at the white man's timber-felling centres in the forest. They are homeless proletarians in the saddest and worst sense of that word.

This migration of the population from the interior to the region of the Lower Ogowe creates serious social and economic problems. In itself it is natural, and it is hardly possible to stop it, for the population here is diminishing in number, and it is far from large enough to provide the timber-trade with the amount of labour-power which is needed for the exploitation of the forests. There must, therefore, be migrations from the interior, if industry and commerce are not to be crippled. In our district the immigrant proletarians are, so far as I can judge, a fifth at any rate of the population; they may be more.

But to what extent is it permissible that the interior be depopulated for the benefit of the Ogowe forests, and our district burdened with proletarians? For a depopulation of the interior is already setting in of itself, in consequence partly of the epidemic of influenza which raged after the war, and partly of the famine which prevailed during the same period, not to mention the ravages of sleeping-sickness. The subsequent movement of so many of its capable workers means for each district not only a further diminution of the population, but also a perpetuation of the famine. Who is to clear away the forest and lay out the plantations if none but women, children, and old men are left in the villages? For our district, too, the influx of these men means likewise perpetuation of the famine, for being engaged on nothing but the obtaining of timber, they can lay out no plantations and they increase the consumption of the already short supply of the foodstuffs which are produced here.

In view of these circumstances attempts are made to regulate the migration from the interior, and to limit it so far as it is bound up with the labour needs of the timber trade. Decrees have been issued that only a fixed proportion of the men of a village may enlist to work in the Ogowe forests. It is also laid down that no one may stay here for a long period. Settlement here is absolutely forbidden. At the expiry of their labour contract, that is at the end of one or two years, these workers have to return to their villages.

The recruiting of labourers, therefore, is not carried on just as the European employers would like; it is regulated down to the smallest details. The timber-merchant who wants lumbermen must make his wants known to the authorities. Then he gets permission to go into the interior and secure a definite number of men. The district from which he may get them, and the date by which the recruiting must be finished, are definitely laid down. He often has to travel some 250 miles through forest, swamp, or open country before reaching the villages named. When the contract-period is ended, he cannot just let his labourers go; he must take the whole gang back to their homes. It is hoped that with these measures the evil will be controlled.

There are, however, people with knowledge of the situation, some of them Government officials, who were once in favour of allowing labourers from the interior to bring their wives and children and settle in the Ogowe forests, which offer them permanent employment. These settlers would then themselves lay out plantations and find themselves living under far more favourable conditions in every way than they do at present, when they just camp here without homes. Then, too, they would not make such demands on the foodstuffs produced by the resident natives as they do now.

I am myself inclined to agree with this theory, but have to admit that it takes no account of one important fact. At the end of two or three years, sometimes even sooner, a timber-site, however large it is, has to be abandoned. That does not mean that all the timber in the neighbourhood has been felled, but only that there is none left which can be rolled, without excessive trouble, into the water, or can be removed without too much expense in laying down a temporary line of iron rails. When spots are reached where there is not a recognised proportion of okoumé (false mahogany) trees to the hectare, that being the only kind of tree which is considered worth exporting, the exploitation of that patch of forest is not worth while. The camp has therefore to be transferred elsewhere to a spot, perhaps thirty or sixty miles away, where there is a good supply of okoumé trees, growing on level ground and near the water. This would bring the labourers into the position of having to abandon their plantations just when they were beginning to be productive, which is not till between two and three years after the laying out. On the new site again, not only the labourers but their families would have to live for over a year on the food produced in the district at the expense of its original population, or, if there were no food for them, would have to be supplied with rice imported from Europe or India.

Far-sighted Europeans try to solve the problem of the timber-trade's food supply by having plantations laid out beforehand in the neighbourhood of sites marked out for future exploitation, so that they will be producing just when the tree-felling begins. But this planting for the future is very expensive. First of all, a body of labourers has to be maintained on this far-off spot, and they, since there is no European supervision, generally do nothing at all. The plan is often made impossible anyhow by the shortage of labour, every available man being employed on the cutting and rolling of timber.

I take this opportunity of correcting the mistaken idea that the timber-merchants here all get rich through the sweat of the natives whose labour they hire. If any of them does once in a way make a huge profit, he generally owes it to a stroke of luck which is not likely to be repeated for some time. That was the case this year, for example, with a young man who ventured into the timber-trade without any previous experience. In his unsuspecting simplicity he undertook the exploitation of some fine growths which his rivals seemed to have overlooked. They were, however, in portions of forest from which the timber could be moved only when the water was abnormally high. He was therefore on the high road to losing all the money and trouble which he was putting into the job. But this year the autumn flood reached a height to which it had not risen for years. The timber, which according to ordinary estimates had been cut down entirely in vain, could be got into the water with ease and without any extra expense. The river itself came up to fetch it away. The contractor returned home with a fine balance of profit, and—will come back, enticed by the primeval forest, to make a similar venture when the water is less obliging, to lose everything, and to finish heavily in debt!

Generally speaking, the profits made in the timber-trade cannot be called more than modest considering the amount

of money invested and the hard, comfortless conditions of
life on a timber-site. If anyone works on credit advances,
and is consequently so tied down as to the sale of his timber
that he cannot make full use of any favourable chance that
meets him, he must often feel relieved if he ends his business year free from debt. I have had Europeans with me
for treatment, hard-working business men too, who were
not in a position to repay the hospital the cost of their food
and medicine, but had to ask that the debt might stand over
till better times came.

It is absurd to talk of exploitation by the timber-merchants of the labourers who come down from the interior,
if that means that wages are too low. The work that these
primitive humans do often bears no relation to the wage
which has to be handed out to them at the end of their
contract period. During the first months of it many of
them are almost wholly useless, because they have never
held an axe in their hands and have first of all to learn how
to use one. Nowhere in the world, probably, strange as the
statement may seem, is the total cost of labour higher in
proportion to the work done than in the primeval forest.

And yet, if not in the ordinary sense victims of exploitation, these savages who have become lumbermen are creatures who must excite pity. Coming down from the open
country and the hills of the interior, they cannot stand the
trying climate of the Ogowe depression. They are always
homesick, and all the time. The forest is to them something
uncanny; still more so the water, to which they are unaccustomed. Though unable to swim, they have to deal
with tree-trunks floating in lakes or rivers. Many do soon
become used to it, but many more have to go on from day
to day never losing their dread of the work in the water.
Moreover, the regular daily work demoralises these children
of nature. They always have gnawing at their heart a long-
ing for those intervals of *dolce far niente*, which when they
were at home made up for the periods of hard work.

On the top of all this come health disturbances, which
result from a change of diet. On the long laborious journey
they have already begun to suffer from having to eat rice.

Many arrive already half-ill as the result of it. At the timber-site, indeed, so far as my experience goes, all that is possible is done for them in the matter of food. It is, of course, to the interest of the timber-merchant to keep his labourers as fit as possible. A native who does not get enough to eat shirks work, untroubled about the consequences that may follow. But with the best of will in the matter, the European is often unable to offer his men anything but perpetual rice and salted fish, the two foodstuffs which it is easiest to procure and transport, and which keep in good condition longest. Rice, however, is a food which the savage of Equatorial Africa finds, in general, much less adapted to his constitution than other people do, though why that is so I cannot say. It is certainly to some extent a result of his being too impatient to cook it for more than half the time it needs. The employers have tried to help them by distributing rice ready cooked, and prepared with fat and salt. But they will not have it. They are just savages, who will eat only what they have cooked for themselves in their small pots over a smoky fire. The rice, then, plays havoc with them. They lose weight, they contract stomach- and bowel-troubles, and beriberi develops among them, sometimes in a mild, sometimes in a serious, form.

The harm done by the rice diet would certainly be less if they could obtain instead of the polished stuff, rice which had lost only the outer husk and had retained the inner coat. This, as is now well known, contains the vitamins, and if it is removed, the native gets a vitaminless diet which, if it is used for any considerable time as his sole foodstuff, must cause beriberi.

I, too, have to feed my patients on this polished, vitaminless stuff because in spite of repeated attempts I have never yet been able to procure the other sort in sufficient quantities. Science has proved that the polished rice is a dangerous foodstuff, yet the trade delivers to its customers everywhere only this kind. Are we really living in a progressive age?

To the damaging of the bowel by this rice diet I attribute the fact that dysentery is especially frequent among the black lumbermen just at times when the shortage of bananas and manioc compels them to live on it exclusively. The bowel is then no longer capable of protecting them, as it could if they had their normal diet, from the standing infection produced by the dirty water which these savages of ours drink day after day.

Malaria, too, as well as dysentery, lies in wait for these immigrant lumbermen. In their own hinterland, in the open country and on the elevated plateaux, they know nothing of mosquitoes or malaria. But on the timber-sites these two evils are a serious plague.

Then there are colds and chills. These savages are very susceptible to the damp atmosphere of the forest. Then why do they not spend part of their wages on mosquito nets and blankets? Because mosquito nets are expensive, and being real savages they would rather buy tobacco and trifles than useful things. " Then their masters should be obliged to provide them with mosquito nets and blankets!" Quite right. But they would soon barter the blankets and nets for bananas or baubles of any sort which were offered them by a native from the neighbourhood, just as they dispose of their master's axes and bush-knives for a trifle, and then declare that they are lost.

These labourers from up-country are attacked also in a terrible way by ulcers on their feet. It often happens that a few weeks after their arrival a large proportion of them become incapacitated for work and, as a rule, by the tropical phagedenic ulcer, the worst kind of all. First comes a small spot which festers and discharges, but of which they take no account. Then, in the course of days or weeks, it develops to a sore as large as one's hand, and is terribly painful. And living, as they do, overcrowded in dirty huts without even a pretence of hygiene, they of course infect each other. Sometimes I get a dozen of them at once from the same timber-site, who have developed these phagedenic ulcers by all infection from one single case.

And so we can explain why my hospital, in spite of a big diminution of the population, nevertheless shows a much bigger stream of patients than before. There are fewer people, but more sick, because from the lumbermen of the hinterland a very heavy toll is exacted by the change of climate, their new diet, and the diseases already prevalent here.

What a tragedy it is when half-starved creatures like that, betrayed by their physiognomy as savages from up-country, are deposited, with their miserable little bundles of belongings, at our gate! However often one has to go through the experience, it always moves one to fresh pity. One is seized by an indescribable sympathy with these poor strangers. And how often the sympathy is quite hopeless, since it is evident at the first glance that the visitor will draw his last breath here, far away from his own people, who are waiting for his return and for the money that he ought to bring with him.

These poorest and most numerous of our guests we call "Bendjabis," because a large proportion of them belong to the Bendjabi tribe.

But the complete absence of any discipline among them makes the work of the hospital so much harder that the sight of them arouses in our hearts a complex feeling of sympathy and despair. Hence I must repeat—to my sorrow —that my hospital is no longer what it used to be.

Of order and subordination we require in the hospital only the minimum amount necessary. If a Bendjabi appears of his own accord each morning for his bandaging or his injection or to get his medicine, and does not run away because his turn does not come at once; if when the horn sounds for rations he does not wait more than half an hour before appearing with his plate; if he throws all refuse in its proper place; if he does not steal fowls from the missionary or let the latter catch him plundering his fruit trees or his banana plants; if at cleaning-up time on Saturday afternoon he helps without too much outcry; if, when the lot falls upon him and his condition allows it, he jumps into the canoe ready to paddle it; if, when there are cases and sacks of rice to be unloaded, he lends a hand, even if fate has willed that he has first to be routed out from behind his cooking-pot as fit for the job—anyone who does these things and a few others like them, passes with us for a virtuous and rational being in whom we gladly overlook many shortcomings in other directions.

The Bendjabis, however, are, alas, far below this ideal, modest as it is. Being real savages they are a painful distance "beyond good and evil." The rules which govern life for the hospital inmates are to them mere words which do not concern them. In this matter, indeed, they can appeal to the fact that these rules have never been put before them. The daily proclamation of them as described in my book, *On the Edge of the Primeval Forest*, was given up long ago; the language difficulty had made it useless. Formerly we could manage with a knowledge of the Galloa and Pahouin languages; to-day there are some ten languages spoken in our wards. Dominic, G'Mba's successor, who has lived for some time in the interior, can express himself in several of them, but not in all, so that we have to deal with many patients with whom we cannot exchange an intelligible word.

What this means was brought home to us in a tragic fashion one day by the case of a poor savage who came to us with a strangulated hernia. We had to place him on the operating-table without being able to explain to him what we were going to do, and while he was being fixed in position horror painted itself on his face; he certainly believed that he had fallen among cannibals! But with the anæsthetic there came an end to his terror, and when he woke, free from his torturing pain, an understanding look spread over his face, and he gave us a smile of gratitude. But, alas, it was impossible to save his life! Never have I used the operating-knife with such deep emotion as I did that day.

That we can trouble them so little with talk is an encouragement to these Bendjabis to rise superior to everything that can be expected of a guest in our hospital.

Anyone who gives a Bendjabi an order has to wait in vain for any sound or movement which may indicate whether he has been understood or not, and whether or not the order will be obeyed. He might as well give it to a log of wood.

Of what is meant by property they have no notion, and they steal from the other inmates whatever they can, even robbing of his food a patient who cannot leave his bed.

Hence I live in a state of perpetual anxiety as to when these savages will cause us difficulties with the mission. Only a few days ago M. Herrmann brought me two who had been caught in the act of carrying off nuts from one of the mission station palm trees. They were two miserable dysentery patients who could scarcely walk about, and into whose hands we should not have ventured to put a broom for the Saturday clean-up. Yet they climbed the palm tree, and managed successfully the troublesome job of freeing the nut with a bush-knife from the thorny growth around it. Fortunately, M. Herrmann smoothes over all such difficulties with Solomon-like wisdom and Christian kindness.

But we are not tried only by the entire absence of discipline in our savages; we suffer from their absolute inability to understand that anything can be valuable. The hospital being so near the forest it is really not at all hard for them to get firewood. But, as it is rather less trouble, they prefer to burn the beams and planks which I procure with so much trouble and such heavy expense, and having no place which I can make secure with lock and key, I am quite at a loss for a way of keeping my precious timber safe from them.

This unsuccessful struggle, repeated day after day, to produce in these savages some notion of what is meant by value, is a trial of patience and nerves as severe as any that anyone could imagine.

My poultry is, of course, no safer from the Bendjabis than is that of the missionaries. Many a fowl has already ended its days in a cooking-pot to provide an evening banquet.

I am describing only the worst of our Bendjabis, but the worst are many in number. If they remain some time, they do, through the example of others, get somewhat accustomed to regularity and order, but fresh ones are continually coming with whom we have to begin again at the beginning, and this uses up our nervous vigour much more than the work does. We are learning the full meaning of the interesting fact that we are allowed to spend out life among savages.

And yet, however often we groan over the Bendjabis—and one of our household sayings is : " How beautiful Africa would be without its savages !"—we do feel that there is a link between them and us. When the new doctor launches out into angry denunciation of them, I point out to him with what regret and affection he will look back upon them when he is again in Europe. Many of them are, indeed, men who have become human animals, not merely savages, but creatures who, through living far from their homes and coming under so many injurious influences, have sunk even below the level of savages. They do not even feel any gratitude for what we do for them. Their interpretation is that we behave in this way because it is a sure way to get rich, and they tell this to their comrades on the timber-site, as I know from those who have heard them do so.

There are others, however, who do become attached to us. How many a savage of whom we had unpleasant reminiscences and of whom we were confident that after the numerous scoldings he had received he would have taken away no good report of us, has run to greet us with a beaming face when one of our journeys has brought us close to his timber-site ! How often, as a canoe is passing, a hearty greeting floats over to us from someone in the row of paddling Bendjabis !

I daresay we should have fewer difficulties with our savages if we could occasionally sit round the fire with them and show ourselves to them as men, and not merely as medicine-men and custodians of law and order in the hospital. But there is no time for that. All three of us, we two doctors and Nurse Kottmann, are really so overwhelmed with work that the humanity within us cannot come out properly. But we cannot help it. For the present we are condemned to the trying task of carrying on the struggle with sickness and pain, and to that everything else has to give way.

Sometimes I have to deal with natives who were in Europe as soldiers during the war. The one with whom I get on best is a Pahouin who never boasts of any heroic deeds. Coming home safe and sound he entered the service of a white man, three hours above Lambarene, as cook. Then, while playing one day with his master's sporting gun, he got his right elbow shattered, partly through his own fault, partly through that of the boy who was handling it with him. He was brought to us during the night and by the light of a lantern I staunched the blood-flow and removed the splinters.

Through questions which I put to the man about the gold crowns on some of his teeth, I learnt that my patient had been in Europe and in military service, though he had said nothing about it. These crowns did not imply any damage to the teeth, but the black soldiers made a practice of getting them put on in order to make an impression on their people at home. Otherwise the warrior from Europe had in clothing and behaviour become a native again like his neighbours, except that his experience had made him really serious; it weighed him down like a burdensome secret. " In the village (he said to me) they are always asking me to tell them about the war, but I can't do it. And they wouldn't understand if I did. It was all so horrible, so horrible!"

The whole time that the wounded man spent in the hospital I kept with us the boy who had let off the gun, for fear lest the relatives should do him a mischief, or even carry him off so as to extort a big ranson for him. He was told off to assist in the kitchen and with the washing-boiler, and he gave useful help to Nurse Kottmann. To my great joy, too, I was able to bring about an agreement as to compensation between him and his victim. The former was to pay a sum of money worth about 100 shillings in monthly instalments of 10s., and give a goat as well. Custom demands that in every case of possibly fatal injury something living must be handed over. If the victim had lost his arm, the other would have had to buy him a wife.

Many a serious conversation did I have with this native who was suffering thus from his experience of the war. Madame Herrmann also won his regard, and whenever she came into the hospital for the evening prayers, he was one of the first to take his place.

In December, a Bendjabi is brought to us from a timber-site on Lake Azingo. He and his mates had devoured in three days a large elephant which had been killed in the neighbourhood, and he had got a lump of hard elephant flesh stuck in his throat.

The Canadian, who has been here since early in October, and for whom we had to open one abscess after the other, is now beginning to walk. He had become a skeleton, and I had almost given up all hope of saving him.

And I have been a patient myself for weeks. Ulcers on my feet from my first residence here, though perfectly healed over, have broken out again, because of repeated injuries received during building operations, and they give me much trouble. I hobble about as well as I can, but when they are very bad I get myself carried down to the hospital. I must be down below the whole day, else no building gets done. The worst of the ulcers is that the continual burning pain causes extreme nervous irritation.

On December 12th one room is ready for use in the little house meant for the doctor and white patients. I had worked on into the night with the black carpenter to get the doors and shutters fixed, and did well to refuse to listen to the new doctor and Nurse Kottmann, who wanted to forbid me all building work because of the condition of my feet, for the very next day in trooped together six European patients, who had to be housed. Among them was a lady with a small child, the condition of both of whom gave cause for much anxiety. Her husband was ill also. One of the men, as soon became clear, was in the first stage of sleeping-sickness. A few days later another European came in, so that at Christmas we had, with the Canadian, eight white patients to provide for. Without that room, which was ready just in time to take four of them, I should not have known how to put them up. Two are taken in by M. and Madame Herrmann. The native carpenter, who wanted to leave me in the lurch because he did not like being hurried so much, is reconciled by a handsome present.

On Christmas Eve there is a general feeling of depression. The lady, who is lodged in our house, feels very miserable, and while we others sing carols round a decorated palm tree, Nurse Kottmann sits on the edge of her bed and tries to stop her tears. On the hillside below there is a light burning far into the night, for the Canadian is celebrating his recovery with his room-mates. He can walk about again, and even help me with the building.

CHAPTER IV

Spring, 1925. More Buildings Needed

WE begin the new year badly, for all three of us are unwell. The new doctor is in bed with boils; Mlle Kottmann feels miserably out of sorts; and I am suffering more than ever from the ulcers on my feet, which are spreading. I cannot get a shoe on so I drag myself about in wooden ones. We get through the work after a fashion, but that is all.

But we are immensely cheered by the condition of the sleeping-sickness patient, who is improving every day. His fever has gone, and his torturing headaches are lessening. His case shows us once more that in every case of illness which begins with fever or headaches or rheumatism, the first thing to do is to examine the blood microscopically. Without the information that affords, an incipient case of sleeping-sickness might pass for one of malaria and be treated with quinine, which would do no good and would lose valuable time. Moreover, the new remedies work with certainty only in the first and second stages. Of course, the patient first learns what his illness is when he is on the way to recovery.

And now there comes a piece of news which gives us all fresh courage. A third doctor, Dr. Mark Lauterburg, of Berne, will be here in a few weeks. Dr. Nessmann and I are already convinced that we two cannot manage alone. The surgical work still has to be curtailed; to do what is needed would mean operating on three mornings a week, and that is impossible. The ordinary work keeps us so busy that we should not know how to get three mornings for it. And here, moreover, there falls on the surgeon all the petty attendant work, before and after an operation, which in Europe can be left to the nurses and the orderlies. For this we have not sufficient strength, nor would our exhausting activities allow us to come to the actual operation fresh enough. The new doctor already knows, alas, how closely connected are Africa, fatigue, and nervous irritation.

On the other hand, I am more strongly convinced than ever that a hospital in the primeval forest achieves its object only if surgery occupies its proper place in the work. In a land where hernia and elephantiasis are so common, the help that the knife can give must not be wanting. A successful operation conveys a message into the remotest districts, and gives sufferers confidence in the ability of the the white doctor. We must, therefore, so we decided, get a medical man here whose work will be chiefly surgery. And now he is actually on the point of embarking!

The third doctor, who must bring with him (so logic demands!) a second, possibly even a third, nurse, compels me to think of more building. The three-roomed cottage which was meant for the second doctor and the white patients, can now be considered as possibly a house for doctors only. Anyhow, the two rooms provided for the white patients would in the long run not have been sufficient, as I saw at Christmas. How sorry I felt for the four patients, who had to be quartered together in the small and low room which had just enough space for four camp beds! If there had been a dying man among them, where else could I have put him?

I have also to think about providing some rooms in which our reserves of household things, linen, bedding, and foodstuffs, can be stored, together with bandages and drugs. All these supplies are at present kept in piled-up chests and packing-cases, many of which stand in a shed which is far from providing proper protection against either rain or thieves. To get out any object that is wanted at once, one has to summon some natives and shift a dozen heavy cases. And how Dr. Nessmann and I shudder when any drug has to be taken from our reserve!

People in Europe can hardly form an idea of the amount and variety of stores which must be provided for the regular conduct of a hospital in an African forest. Formerly I arranged to keep myself supplied for six months ahead. Now I calculate for a year.

Of the land belonging to the mission station, but placed at my disposal, there is still a piece vacant which has just room for a house about 60 feet long and 20 feet broad. I determine, therefore, to undertake a big building which will have room within it for the white patients, and also for our stores.

It must be built on piles with a corrugated-iron roof, and contain ten rooms. The Canadian, Mr. Crow, who is now almost completely well again, goes with a good crew, which is at my disposal for a few days, to fetch the hard-wood piles from a small side-stream about eighteen miles up the river. Each evening the new doctor and I take spades and level a portion of the site. The people at the N'Gômô saw-pit promise to do their best to deliver the timber, so there is hope that all the preparations will be so far completed by the beginning of the dry season at the end of May that we can then begin building.

On January 17th the native carpenter's wife is released by death from her sufferings. By careful nursing we have at least managed to save her from getting bed-sores. That is what makes sleeping-sickness as an illness so especially pitiable. We all followed her body to its last resting-place.

But now for a long time her husband will do no work. Mourning means holiday, and there is no shaking that custom. For weeks the widower must sit in his hut in torn clothing and touch nothing. And this is a sacred duty. In their customs, at any rate, the negroes honour their dead more than we do.

It follows that I must finish the house for the two doctors without help, and for the present Dr. Nessmann remains dependent on the hospitality of M. and Madame Herrmann.

Mr. Crow, the Canadian, who was to have started for home on February 20th, got a bad sunstroke while on a journey to visit a friend, and this weakened his resisting power so much that his body succumbed to the infection over which, after months of struggle, he was on the point of triumphing. Persistent fever set in with new abscesses, and his life was once more in danger. What an amount of anxiety and work this one white patient has cost us!

On January 27th Mlle Kottmann and I together just escape death by drowning. We were returning with a good crew after nightfall in a heavily laden canoe from a factory where we had made many purchases. I gave an order not to keep too near the bank, because on our journey out I had noticed in the water a huge mass of foliage belonging to a fallen tree. We had travelled some distance when I began to suspect that we were after all too near the bank. The crew denied it, and I quieted my suspicions with the reflection that the eyes of these children of nature would certainly see better than mine. But I was suddenly seized with an inexplicable feeling of unrest. I jumped up and compelled the crew to turn the canoe towards the middle of the river. At that very moment there loomed up out of the water the huge mass of the tree, and we just managed to scrape past it. But for that turn we should have dashed into it at full speed, have been dazed by the impact, and have been thrown into the water. One can never rely on the natives here, not even in things which they understand from long practice. They are so thoughtless that you can never tell what they are going to do.

On the day following this adventure there arrives the long and eagerly awaited hospital motor-boat. It comes from kind friends in Sweden, who have been collecting money for it since 1922. We do not know how to express our gratitude for it. It means for us all travelling more safely, more quickly, and more comfortably. Completely covered by a canvas awning, it will protect us from both sun and rain, if the latter is not too heavy. Best of all, the travelling will cost not more than by canoe, as might have been thought, but less. What we have had to offer a crew in the way of food, wages, and presents is considerably more than the outlay on petrol and oil for the same length of journey.

Built with a fairly narrow hull, the motor-boat makes good way against the strong current, and it draws little water, so as to be all right in shallow water during the dry season. Its length is about 28 feet, its width 5 feet, and it can carry a ton weight. The extremely simple single-cylindered motor is of 3½ horse-power, and uses about 2½ pints of petrol per hour. Against the current and heavily laden it makes 7 to 8 kilometres (four and a quarter to five miles) per hour, in still water rather more than 12 (seven and a half miles).

This kind of motor-boat is used by almost all timber-merchants here, and it has proved itself a reliable craft. Ours bears a Swedish name : "Tack sa Mycket," i.e., "Many thanks."

On February 10th a large and well-appointed motor-boat brings an ailing Dutch lady up from Cape Lopez. Its owner, Mr. Drew, a friendly Englishman, is kind enough to take back with him the Canadian, who is now getting better. We think him fit for the journey, but, as he still needs bandaging, Dr. Nessmann goes with him to the coast.

For ten days I am again the only doctor. About this time we almost always have with us half a dozen white patients. One of them, a Pole named Rochowiack, who came on account of a wounded foot, goes down, while here, with blackwater fever. He gives himself up for lost, because he had seen, in Rhodesia, seven cases of it, all of which ended fatally. I, on the other hand, can comfort him with the assurance that I have never yet lost a black-water-fever patient.

Once more I have found corroboration of the statement that heavy doses of quinine taken suddenly by people not accustomed to the drug do in some way or other cause the outbreak of this fever. M. Rochowiack felt himself somewhat feverish, took some quinine, though he was not in the habit of using it, and a good deal of it, too, as exhorted to do by the patients who shared his room. The next morning he had blackwater fever. Under what conditions quinine produces that wholesale destruction of the red blood-corpuscles, which we know to be the precursor of this fever, we cannot yet say, and, indeed, many points connected with this disease are still a mystery.

As soon as ever he was fairly well, M. Rochowiack began helping me with the building work. He is a joiner and carpenter, and I learnt many things from him. He instructed me in the simplified method of timber construction which is widely followed in S. Africa, where he had lived a considerable time.

Just now we have with us two natives who have wounds caused by human teeth. One of them got his while trying to arrest a dilatory debtor. Biting as a method of offence or defence is more frequent with Africans than with us. " The worst bite (says Joseph) is that of the leopard; worse still is that of a poisonous snake; worse still a monkey's bite, but quite the worst of all that of a man." There is some truth in this. I have had occasion in Africa to see about a dozen cases of the human bite, and all showed at once symptoms of severe infection. In two cases a general blood-poisoning seemed imminent, although the victims came to me within a few hours. One of these two victims will have to lose the end joint of one finger.

Cases of leprosy are continually coming to us, though there would be many more if the treatment were not so tedious ! For it is only at the end of several weeks, as a rule, that the sick person notices an improvement. Many find their patience exhausted before that, and will not let us keep them any longer. They usually come only to obtain and take home with them some Chaulmoogra oil which has been prepared for drinking, that is, has been diluted with sesame- and peanut-oil. They have been for a long time familiar with this treatment, but they are unwilling to learn that much better results can be obtained if this is followed by a series of injections of Chaulmoogra-oil derivatives, because that requires too long a stay in the hospital. We hope, however, to get results which will convince them. I have, indeed, to allow that life in our overcrowded wards is not a pleasant experience.

On March 16th, on my return from a two-day journey in the motor-boat, I see standing by Dr. Nessmann on the landing-stage a slender figure in the elegantly careless attitude of a cavalry officer. It is the new doctor, Dr. Mark Lauterburg.

The beds in the wards for the surgical patients have just been finished, so he can begin work at once, and the first case which is entrusted to his knife is a sleeping-sickness patient with an empyema which requires a rib resection. The poor creature is a savage from the interior called Yezu, and he has been with us for months. The sleeping-sickness seems to have been mastered, but he, no doubt, lacks strength to get over the empyema. We like him because of his gentle nature. How grateful he is for the soups which are made for him! " When I am well (he says) I will stay with you for ever."

During his second operation, at which we others are with him, Dr. Lauterburg is startled by a native, who rushes into the room crying out: " They are trying to kill the Doctor's chickens "—" they " meaning the Bendjabi, who can just crawl about, and his accomplices. I should have been surprised if they had *not* used for the benefit of their cooking-pot the time when doctors and nurses were all engaged indoors!

In the small hours of March 19th a European patient died suddenly of sunstroke, though the day before he had been discussing plans for his voyage home. He was buried in the Catholic cemetery on the same afternoon as Joseph's mother, who was a fine old woman.

How difficult to write are the letters in which I have to tell the relatives of a European who has died here about his last days and his death!

Out of affection for me, Joseph appears again for work after only three weeks of mourning for his mother, which I think very much to his credit. " The Doctor is a slave to his work, and Joseph is the Doctor's slave," he says. The native carpenter, Monenzalie, now a widower, returns at the same time. He is one of the best carpenters in the whole district, and could any day get a better-paid and much pleasanter post. If he decides in my favour, it is a result of personal attachment.

Since Dr. Lauterburg's arrival there have been operations

three mornings a week. His name among the natives is
"N'Tschinda-N'Tschinda," i.e., "The man who cuts
boldly." Dr. Nessmann they call "Ogula," i.e., "The
Captain's son," "the Captain" meaning me. The men tell
each other that in return for his loyal service I am going
to buy him a wife in Europe, so that he can marry as soon
as he gets back.

In the matter of accident surgery, N'Tschinda-
N'Tschinda has some difficulty in converting himself to
acceptance of the principle on which I act, of non-amputa-
tion. We must, that is to say, here avoid amputation in
cases when, in spite of some danger to the patient's life,
it is done in Europe as a matter of course. Else the report
would spread to the ends of our world that the doctor at
Lambarene cuts people's arms and legs off, and that would
frighten numbers from coming here for help.

Hitherto I have had no cause to repent of having aimed
at the reputation of being a doctor who leaves arms and
legs in their places, but my success in this I owe to methyl-
violet. Every traumatic wound of a limb, however serious
it may look—and most of them do look serious—is treated
with this methyl-violet. My own experience is that it is
successful only if the dressing is kept moist. Dry dressings,
or wet ones which get dry, may actually be dangerous,
because the methyl-violet, in its state of very fine division,
may dry into a scab, and thus form a covering layer beneath
which the infection can spread still further. Boils, whitlows,
and all suppurating foci which cannot drain easily may
therefore give very poor results from treatment with methyl-
violet. The dressing must be kept always moist, so as to
avoid any dry deposit. Then only is the drug safe, and
then only can the dye produce its full effect.

An open wound is therefore covered with gauze which
has just been dipped in a weak solution of methyl-violet,
and this is kept moist by constant application outside it
of gauze which has been dipped in sterilised water. Moreover, owing to the simplicity of the remedy the dressing can
be wrapped in waterproof material to prevent evaporation,
and this can be done even with badly infected wounds on

which a moist dressing would otherwise be a mistake.
Methyl-violet also makes possible the use of a moist bandage
when one would otherwise have to abstain from using it,
and so lose the result it produces. In severe cases we also
resort to long-continued sprinkling with a weak solution
of methyl-violet. This drug has the great advantage of
not causing irritation; it has, on the contrary, a decidedly
soothing effect, as I have often observed.

Burns I treat from the third or fourth day with a 3 per
cent methyl-violet ointment, after having applied to them,
in the usual way, bandages with tannic ointment.

Dr. Lauterburg has been quite surprised by the results
of our procedure in cases where amputation seemed to be
demanded. The most convincing of them he found in a
compound and septic fracture of the lower leg, which was
brought to us with gas gangrene already beginning.

Thanks to our complete abstinence from amputation we
can now resort to it in absolutely necessary cases without
endangering our reputation. Occasionally it happens that
natives even ask for it of their own accord.

Dr. Lauterburg has now operated on quite a number of
hernia cases, and had ample opportunity of convincing himself that such operations do, as a rule, offer more difficulties
here than in Europe, for the reason that one almost always
meets with extensive displacements. These are produced
by the various attempts which the natives make to reduce
the hernia, and thereby the tissues get mishandled and
pinched.

Elephantiasis, too, has its turn on the table. On April
1st we attack a growth weighing 72 lb., on a man from
near Samkita. The weight of it had for a long time condemned him to inactivity, and it is of such a size that he
can use it as a cushion to sit upon. Although he is still
fairly young, he looks like an old man. The operation lasts
from 10 o'clock till 3 in the afternoon, and the handling of
such a mass makes heavy demands on the physical strength
of all three of us. We follow in our procedure the method,
first made public in 1913 by Dr. Ouzilleau, of cutting the
tumour down the middle as if it were a pear. This facili-

tates the search for the blood vessels, and makes possible
the complete prevention of hæmorrhage.

That very day there turns up unexpectedly a helper for
the building operations, viz., a young Swiss, named Schatzmann. Having heard of my need in this direction, he
embarked without any long correspondence with me and
came to give me the most unselfish help. He is a skilled
worker, both as carpenter and foreman, and he takes in
hand the building of the ten-roomed house. What a relief
for me! I have, though, some difficulty in providing him
with accommodation; an unexpected arrival is, in Africa
too, a serious event.

Although the new helper had ideas of building a complete hospital, that is certainly impossible, but when he has
finished his work for me, some of the trading firms will
certainly approach him about building for them. Building
foremen are persons much sought after here, though only
if, as is the case with M. Schatzmann, they can work themselves and get on well with the natives. I have already
had some enquiries about him, as to when he will be free
for another engagement.

There is a tragic happening just about this time. A
dysentery patient who cannot stand upright kills his neighbour, who is as miserable a skeleton as himself; he thought
he meant to steal his rations, for many dysentery patients
have a good appetite up to the very end. We leave the
murderer, who shows no sort of remorse for his act, undis-
turbed, as it is evident that he will soon follow his victim
into the other world. And so he does.

At the end of April we lose close together two patients
after operations, and there are not a few deaths to register
among the medical patients. This so depresses us that we
just drag ourselves about to our work.

At the beginning of the month the work on the ten-
roomed house threatens to come to a standstill because we
have no more beams, although some have been lying here
for weeks. M. Mathieu, a Samkita timber-merchant, has

sent me thirty fine hardwood beams in recognition of my having had under my care for a long time one of his European staff who was seriously ill. But the beams are 25 cm. square, while I want some of 8 cm., and it would be only a small job to saw each of these into four. That would give me 120 beams of the size I want, and enable me to make a beginning, but I can find no sawyers, though I have been trying for weeks. If I wanted five-and-twenty native clerks, I should have fifty applying to-morrow. But sawyers? No.

How true it is, after all, that civilisation does not begin with reading and writing but with manual labour. Because we have no manual workers here, real progress is impossible. The natives learn to read and write without learning at the same time to use their hands. With these accomplishments they obtain posts as salesmen and clerks, and sit about in white suits. But manual work is despised.

Had I any say in the matter, no black man would be allowed to learn to read and write without being apprenticed to some trade. No training of the intellect without simultaneous training of the hands! Only so can there be a sound basis for further advance. How ridiculous it seems to me to read that Africa is being opened up to civilisation because a railway has been built to this place, a motor-car has got through to that, and an air service is being established between two other localities. That does not mean any real gain. "How far are the natives becoming efficient men?" That is the one thing that matters, and efficient men they can become only through religious and moral teaching combined with manual work. All other things have meaning only when this foundation has been well and truly laid. And of all handicrafts that of the sawyer is, once more, the most important, for he turns tree-trunks into beams and planks with which we can build houses to live in. Before there were any sawmills, our ancestors sawed them by hand, and if the natives do not advance by that same road they remain just savages, even if one or another of them, as a commercial or a Civil Service clerk, earns money enough to get his wife silk stockings and high-heeled shoes from Europe. Both they and their descendants will continue, in that case, to live in bamboo huts.

For the sawing of beams and planks out of a tree-trunk the latter is fixed above a pit, about 6 feet wide, and 12 feet or more long. It is then taken in hand by two sawyers with a long, straight saw, one of them standing on the trunk, the other in the pit. The path the saw-blade must take is carefully marked beforehand with corresponding lines above and below, and the special skill is shown in keeping the saw perpendicular and on the lines. This requires some practice, but two good sawyers, working well together, can produce ten beams or planks a day. This kind of work, however, though for this district the most valuable of all, is held in least respect as being too simple and too fatiguing. Consequently the people live in miserable little huts when they might live in houses of mahogany, and I cannot get even a couple of sawyers to cut up some big beams into smaller ones!

In this difficulty help comes to me through an inflamed throat. The wife of a timber-merchant whom I know to have two good sawyers in his service, comes to us in April to be treated for a rather severe attack. Her husband cannot but send the sawyers here, and place them at my disposal. A few days see the job finished, and I have 120 small beams. The new house can now have its roof put on.

On May 3rd I go with Dr. Nessmann to a timber-site lying north of this place, where severe dysentery has broken out and claimed many victims. Our journey takes us first to the end of Lake Azingo, forty-four miles away, and there we leave the motor-boat. Then in two small canoes we travel fifteen miles up a small stream with a strong current, where we are plagued by tsetse flies. At the timber-site we examine the whole body of workers, give advice as to the treatment of those who have mild attacks, and take the bad cases with us. This is Dr. Nessmann's first visit to a timber-site. On May 5th we are back in Lambarene, thanks to the motor-boat, which manages the forty-four miles up-stream in well under a day.

On this journey I write my last letter to my father, but it never reaches him, for death called him home that very day, May 5th.

Through a series of new experiences N'Tschinda-N'Tschinda learns that surgery in Africa is not what it is in Europe. It fell out that in a quarrel with another man —about a woman—a native got a blow in his forearm with a bush-knife. His relatives, in a body, bring him to us, and it is found necessary to suture the wound, which our surgeon does in the most approved professional way. Now when a patient is so injured that he cannot cook for himself, our rule is that someone stops to wait on him, and this man's relatives appointed unanimously to the post one of their number, who accepted it as being a matter of course. But Dr. Lauterburg is never really satisfied with the state of his patient in spite of his faultless suturing. The wound seems to heal well, but the man himself begins to fall off in condition; he lurches about when coming to have the wound dressed, is confused, and loses the power of speech. N'Tschinda-N'Tschinda finds himself quite non-plussed by an infection which produces such general symptoms, but with no fever and the wound healing up so well. . . . " Poison ! " I ejaculate, as soon as he draws my attention to the case, for anyone who has worked here for a long time always assumes poison as a possible cause of any symptoms which are otherwise inexplicable. So on some honourable pretext the attendant who has hitherto cooked for the poisoned man is given work in the hospital, and his victim gets his food only from the hands of one of our orderlies. Then the disturbing effects pass slowly, very slowly, away.

A little later the matter is cleared up. The man left here was the man who had had the difference with the patient and had inflicted the wound, and he had been obliged to undertake the work as compensation. Then he succumbed to the temptation to misuse his opportunity and get rid of his rival. Although we breathed not a word of what was happening, the relatives became suspicious, so to prevent them from killing the poisoner and adding a second drama to the first, the latter was enlisted for personal service to Nurse Kottmann in the doctor's house, where he worked willingly and well at washing and water-carrying.

That there is an extensive use of poison in Equatorial Africa is only too true. One day—it is a story of several months ago—there came to us with his relatives a sick man in a most miserable condition. He, too, had lost his power of speech. At first I thought it might be a general blood-poisoning as a result of infection in some small injury, but the heart was all right, and the sick man was at times so thoroughly himself that the assumption seemed a very questionable one. Since he refused bananas and rice, I tried to feed him with milk, but the milk which his relatives offered he refused to take. That roused my suspicions. I therefore seized the opportunity one day, when his relatives were out of sight, to give him some milk myself. This he drank greedily, so after that he got all his food and drink from one of our orderlies, and these he never refused. The explanation we gave to the relatives was that he needed specially prepared food and drink. However, he was too far gone to be saved.

I remember, too, that once, when I was treating a European whose condition I could not explain, I found some excuse for getting rid of the black servants who had come with him. That does not mean that I had any direct suspicions of the cook and the boy; they may have merely been too unobservant to prevent an attempt at poisoning by someone else through them.

For investigation of the nature of the poisons used I have never had time; but they are usually slow ones. Let it suffice to say that in a number of cases since 1913 I have tested animal charcoal as a remedy. Whenever I find myself suspicious, the patient gets animal charcoal in water to drink; if there is none to be had, ordinary charcoal will do. Joseph watches me knowingly when I prepare " the black medicine." Perhaps we shall some day have doctors enough here to let one of us devote himself to the investigation of poisons.

But there are also involuntary poisonings to be taken into account. Of the roots, bark, and leaves which the natives use for all sorts of diseases, many have the peculiarity of irritating the kidneys severely, others of attacking the heart. Some of them, if given in excessive quantities, endanger life itself. A number of cases of kidney disease, before which we have to confess ourselves powerless, can be traced back to some drink that was taken as medicine. If the heart beats too slowly, it may be assumed that the sufferer has been given seeds of the strophantus bush, which grows here in huge quantities. There are also cases of delirium which arise from poisoning.

Europeans who let themselves be treated with the medicines used by the natives, paying for this sometimes a heavy penalty, are not so few in number as one would like to think.

CHAPTER V

Summer, 1925

JUST when we had all our rooms occupied with white
patients, there came an enquiry whether one of us could
go to Cape Lopez to act as locum tenens for the doctor
there, who was suffering from a suppurating wound in one
of his hands. Dr. Lauterburg started for the coast on May
13th, and during the six weeks he was there sick people,
both white and black, gave him plenty to do.

On May 14th an Italian arrived, a Signor Boles, who
among the lagoons south of Cape Lopez had had his arm
badly mauled by a leopard. He had wounded the animal
with a bullet and followed the blood-track, which led him
into a small valley overgrown with reeds. Just as he got
the leopard in view so that he could shoot again, the
negroes, whom he had left in the rear while he followed the
spoor, caught sight of it also, and the loud shout they
raised to warn their master irritated the beast, so that,
instead of retreating, it sprang on the Italian before he
could shoot again. He drew back, and used the butt end of
his rifle to defend himself, but fell, and the leopard seized
his arm, and kept hold of it till the men despatched it with
their spears. It was not till ten days later that he reached
me; the arm was in a bad state, and his general condition
such as to cause much anxiety, but methyl-violet dressings,
used after a sufficient opening of the wounds, were, as
usual, effective.

Yezu, the sleeping-sickness Bendjabi, who was operated
on for empyema, is dying, and we are very sad at not
being able to save him. We are affected also by the death
of another Bendjabi, called N'Dunde, who has been here
a long time and has cried over every patient whom we
have had to carry out to his last resting-place. And just
now there are many deaths. There have been days on

which we have had to record as many as three, but that
is because so many patients are brought to us in a dying
condition.

The digging of the graves, which at first caused us so
many difficulties because the natives would not undertake
the work, is now done without our having to trouble about
it, thanks to an arrangement made with Dominic. For each
grave he receives a fixed bonus, for which he has to secure
the necessary four workers and superintend the job. These
four also act as bearers. After the burial they get a present
and an extra big food-ration, and are free from work for
the rest of the day. We cannot, however, get the hospital
inmates to come as mourners. The graveyard is to them
such an uncanny place that they resist all pressure in the
matter.

Yet what a charming place our forest graveyard is! It
is overshadowed by beautiful palms, and no sound breaks
its silence except the songs of the birds. Coffins for the
bodies we cannot provide, having neither planks nor carpenter for them. The bodies are wrapped in linen, and laid
in palm-leaves tied together. So they have a green coffin
which is much more beautiful than one of boards.

At the end of May we have another death among our
white patients, that of an employee of one of the timber-
merchants, who was brought to us in a state of coma.

Now at last the roof of our new house is finished, and
far sooner than it would have been without M. Schatzmann. The flooring, the wall-panelling, and the doors can
be finished, if necessary, by the black carpenter alone,
provided there is wood for them.

The biggest commercial house in the Ogowe district
now offers to put M. Schatzmann in charge of all their
buildings, and he takes my advice to accept this important
and interesting post, though, indeed, he would much prefer
to stay and build me a complete hospital.

Early in June the leopard-bitten Italian is so far restored
to health that he can return to his business at Cape Lopez,
and I go with him to recruit for a short time at the sea-
side. For a whole year I have not had a day out of harness.

But my recruiting does not amount to much. N'Tschinda-N'Tschinda had made such a reputation for us down there, that I am called in again and again by sick people. In particular, some ships in the harbour, on which dysentery had broken out, give me a lot of work. It was the result of drinking polluted water obtained in some harbour away to the south.

Meanwhile we lose by death a man who was waiting for an operation on his large elephantiasis tumour. The cause is pneumonia, a condition which is very frequent at the beginning of the dry season. We also have a fatal case of tetanus, but that condition is very rare here.

During my absence my two colleagues were extremely pleased that a woman who had been bitten by a fish and came to us with a badly poisoned arm, asked of her own accord for amputation. She belongs to the district where the Bendjabi, whose arm we could not help amputating, has preached the usefulness of such an operation. Her case, too, ended satisfactorily.

The two doctors also correctly diagnosed as sleeping-sickness the case of a white lady from near N'Gômô, who came to us with fever and headache. When I got back she was already on the road to recovery. We also took in another white lady for her confinement.

Still another, whom I had attended in similar circumstances some months before, came from the interior with her baby, accompanied by her husband. She was now suffering from mental disease, but fortunately there were already some rooms in the new house finished, so that I could accommodate her till she left for Europe. It was a very serious case.

Towards the end of June the dysentery cases increased to an alarming extent, and we did not know where to put the sufferers. It is well known that there are two kinds of dysentery, amœbic and bacillary.

The former is caused by amœbæ, unicellular organisms which settle in the large intestine and bore into its walls, giving rise to hæmorrhage. The remedy for this kind is emetin, a drug which is obtained from ipecacuanha bark and has been in use since 1912. From 8 to 10 centigrammes of emetin dissolved in sterilised water is given for several days running by subcutaneous injection, and the injections are repeated after an interval of a few days. Unfortunately, this drug is terribly expensive.

The other kind of dysentery, that produced by bacteria, we are not so well prepared to deal with. Every possible remedy is being tried, but so far without satisfactory results.

Both kinds may occur together. Formerly it was the amœbic which was commonest here; now we often have cases of mixed infection, especially in men who come from the timber-sites.

What work is caused us by the dysentery patients who can no longer move about, and who dirty everything where they sit or lie! Many have to be fed by hand because they are too weak to carry a spoon to their mouths. And the care of them is all the more laborious because the natives will not stir a finger to help; to such disgusting work there is no bringing them. We therefore often have to do it all ourselves, and if there ever *is* a black man who will help, he is loaded with presents and smothered with praise.

Our great concern is to prevent the permanent infection of the hospital with dysentery germs. Anyone who tastes food or water that is polluted in any way with dysenteric excrement catches the disease. Anyone who has washed his hands in polluted water, or touched polluted earth with them, and then puts a finger in his mouth, may get dysentery. Anyone who washes his cooking utensils in polluted water may also become infected.

We have, therefore, to take the greatest care that the dysentery patients pollute nothing and do not mix with the others. I ought to have wards for them only, but I have not. Nor have I even a piece of ground on which I could build some. The only thing I can do is to build cubicles for them in the existing wards. To leave them permanently in these confined spaces, where they get hardly any sun or air, is impossible. Yet if I leave them in the sun, they pollute in the most conscienceless way every place they visit. With them warnings are no help, and supervision is impossible. If only I could provide a room for them with a good fence round it!

It is useless for us to preach carefulness to the patients. They are told to use only water from the spring. But the river is only twenty paces away while the spring is a hundred, so they fetch their water from the former. It is forbidden to do any cooking jointly with a dysentery patient, but they do cook with them and eat out of the vessel into which the latter have put their dirty fingers.

A Bendjabi, being treated for ulcers, discovered among the dysentery patients a man from his own district, and now he shares with him his ward-space and his cooking-pot. We drag him away and explain to him the risk he runs. In the evening he is again in the cubicle, and every time he is removed he manages to get back. " Do you want to kill yourself? " Dr. Nessmann asked him. " Better be with my brother and die, than not see him," was the answer. Home-sickness is with them stronger than fear of death. Of course the dysentery does not let this self-offered victim escape.

Since our number rose to three so that we can find time to make liberal use of the microscope, we have proved that angkylostomiasis is much more prevalent here than we believed. It is well known that attention was first drawn to this disease when many of those who worked on the S. Gotthard tunnel began to suffer from severe anæmia. The cause was discovered to be small worm about a centimetre long in the small intestine. Later on it was established as a fact that this disease occurs wherever men work in damp earth which is never exposed to cold, as is the case in tunnels, mines, and other hot places.

Infection comes in a remarkable way. The larva out of which the worm develops lives in water or in damp earth, and enters the human body, not through the mouth in drinking-water but through the skin. It stays for a time in the lung, but then settles in the small intestine, where it develops into the worm. There is no known protection against this disease and it can even be caught by washing

one's hands in apparently clean water. The regular course
of infection is indicated by bowel disturbances with increasing weakness and anæmia. The sufferer loses blood continually through the injuries caused by the worm to the
mucosa of the intestine.

Whenever, therefore, a sick person, whether white or
black, complains of anæmia and weakness, it must be
settled whether or not he has any of these parasites, and
this is done by searching his fæces with the microscope for
the eggs. These are found in large numbers; the worms
themselves much seldomer.

What a relief it is when his condition is found to be
due to this parasite! That means that the mischief is comparatively simple to deal with. Repeated doses of thymol
or carbon tetrachloride drive the worms out, and the
patient recovers his healthy condition. Moreover, these
drugs are not very expensive. They must be used carefully,
however. No alcohol or fat must be taken during their
administration, as these dissolve the thymol. And thymol
is a poison but, being insoluble in water, it passes through
the intestine without being absorbed. If, however, it is
dissolved in alcohol or ether, it gets absorbed and its
poisonous qualities come into play. For that reason every
patient who goes through the treatment here is isolated
for two or three days, and carefully watched. Not even
with Europeans can I be sure that they will of their own
accord obey these instructions. One of them once dis-
regarded them and got a very bad heart attack. Fortunately
I had him, in accordance with my fundamental rule, con-
stantly under observation, and was able to intervene in
time.

With carbon tetrachloride the danger lies in the drug
not being pure, and still containing traces of carbon bisul-
phide. During recent years chenopodium oil has also been
used in treating angkylostomiasis.

The depression we feel at the increase of dysentery is
made worse by news of there being severe famine further
upstream. The districts most severely hit are those border-
ing on the Cameroons and crossed by the N'Djole-Boue-

Makokou caravan route. The root cause of it was the rain which fell during the 1924 dry season and prevented the vegetation which had been cut down from getting dry and being burnt. The prevailing practice is to plant only where the vegetation has been burnt, a procedure which gets rid of the trees and undergrowth and also fertilises the ground with wood-ash. If rain makes this impossible, the people plant nothing, regardless of the consequences. That is how they acted in the districts mentioned above, and also in this one. In our neighbourhood, when the rain stopped, they had not even cut down the vegetation.

It must be added that the laying out of a new plantation is by no means made impossible by the rain, though it is made more difficult. Instead of burning the timber and brushwood, one need only collect them in heaps and then plant in the spaces between the stumps and the heaps. But the people would not make up their minds to do this, so now they have no plants from which they can get any fruit.

In our neighbourhood this fact does not make itself so painfully noticeable, because along the navigable portion of the Ogowe the provision of rice from Europe and India is possible. But in the interior to which the rice would have to be transported for hundreds of kilometres by porters, it can only to a very limited extent be reckoned on as a means of feeding the population. So in those parts there is severe famine, while here the famine is mild. If when the famine began maize had been planted at the right time, the worst stage of the calamity might have been avoided. Maize grows here splendidly, and within four months is ready for reaping. But when food began to run short the natives ate the maize which ought to have been sown. And the height of calamity was reached when the inhabitants of the hardest-hit districts moved into neighbourhoods where there was still some food to be had, and there raided the plantations. Thus these places, too, were reduced to misery, and no one anywhere had the courage to plant anything. It would only have been for the profit of the raiders. So the people sit passively in their villages awaiting the end.

This inability to exert themselves and adapt themselves to difficult circumstances is typical of the natives of Equatorial Africa, and makes them pitiable creatures. There may be no vegetable food from the plantations, but they could secure animal food in the forest and in the open country. Twenty men armed with spears and bush-knives could surround a herd of wild pigs and bag one of them, for these animals are not so fierce as those of Europe. But the starving natives sit in their huts and wait for death just because it is famine time. One cannot say in this country: "Need stimulates invention." It has to be: "Need paralyses into idiocy."

At the end of July I manage to renew the roof of my dwelling-house, which lets in sun and rain through countless holes big and little, for during the last few months we have collected the necessary 3,000 stitched leaves. The merit of this belongs to Dr. Nessmann, who has the gift of bringing home to the hearts of our patients the need for this tribute of leaf-tiles much more convincingly than I can.

When the roof is finished, our canoes are beached to be repaired and re-tarred, all these things being work which must be done during the dry season, when "every day is worth three," as Frère Silvain says, the Catholic missionary who so kindly provides us with vegetables from his big garden. We have no place to make a garden, and should not just now have time to sow if we had one. It is, unfortunately, only for a few weeks that Frère Silvain can make us happy with beans, cabbage, and other vegetables. The garden produces only during the dry season; during the rains it must lie fallow, because cabbages and other vegetables do not flourish in the all-pervading damp heat.

At the beginning of August Dr. Nessmann goes down to Cape Lopez to recruit, a small river-steamer taking him there. Wherever they put in, he is greeted by former patients and his services are claimed afresh. At Cape Lopez he visits the Norwegian whale-fishers, who at this season of the year ply their trade there because the whales come from the southern seas to the Equator to escape the cold. In the southern hemisphere it is, of course, winter, and south winds bring us cool weather.

About this time there arrives from the interior a man who wants to be operated on for a big elephantiasis tumour. Tippoy is his name, and he has dragged himself here from his home over 300 miles away, though he can walk only with quite tiny steps! Here and there he had to traverse the famine district.

Another man, whom we had delivered from a similar tumour, gave the people of his village a regular fright on his return there. When he walked in among them with jaunty steps and looking quite rejuvenated, they thought it was his ghost and scattered in all directions! This he told us himself one day when he came to bring us a goat as a present and more patients for operations. Unfortunately, elephantiasis patients are not all as grateful as he was. One Sunday afternoon Dominic caught one trying to give us the slip, taking with him a blanket and a mosquito net.

At the beginning of September another European comes to us in the early stages of sleeping-sickness. It is an unusually interesting case because the patient has been only twenty-five days in the country, and has never before lived in any colony. It is therefore certain that the infection is quite recent. Nevertheless, he looks quite emaciated, and his face wears that permanent expression of suffering which is characteristic of the advanced stage. I have never watched a case in which the progress of the disease was so rapid, yet after three weeks of treatment he feels as if he had been born again.

Such a cure, which seems to border on the miraculous, gives us great encouragement, and we need it, for the hospital work is getting more and more exhausting through the ever-increasing amount of dysentery. We are all worn out and depressed, trying, as we do, in vain to arrest the growing infection of the hospital. Several patients who came for other complaints have caught dysentery, and some we could not save from death. Some who were on the point of being discharged after an operation have suffered the same fate. How anxiously we ask every morning in the ward where such patients sleep, whether anyone has been seized with dysentery! If anyone comes in complete confidence to entrust himself to our knife, I tremble. Will he not fall a victim to the dysentery?

In vain do we worry ourselves to death in acting as police and trying to ensure a certain amount of obedience to the rules which are directed against dysentery. The inability of our savages to comprehend anything of the kind makes mock of all our efforts. One evening I found a woman filling a bottle close to the landing-stage, where the water is worst polluted. She was the wife of an operation patient, and was getting drinking-water for her husband, using the cover of darkness to get it from the forbidden place. The spring was too far away!

The worst of it is that the sick are beginning to conceal their dysentery, being unwilling to be under supervision and have their freedom curtailed. The other patients do not betray them, and even help them to keep us in ignorance. It was discovered the other day just after we had operated on him, that a man had dysentery, and had had it too for some time, but had concealed it because he knew that we do not operate on persons in that condition.

Through the extra work entailed by all this our staff is getting quite exhausted. It is astonishing that our orderlies continue to work with us; it can certainly be no pleasure to work for doctors with nerves as frayed as ours are. The Bendjabis naturally take advantage of our condition of overwork and worry to show us their worst side.

One day, in my despair at some of them who had once more been drawing polluted water, I threw myself into a chair in the consulting-room and groaned out: "What a blockhead I was to come out here to doctor savages like these!" Whereupon Joseph quietly remarked: "Yes, Doctor, here on earth you are a great blockhead, but not

in heaven." He likes giving utterance to sententious re-
marks like that. I wish he would support us better in our
efforts to hinder the spread of dysentery!

While we are thus overwhelmed with work in the hospital I have also to think about making good the whole of
our leaf-tile roofing in view of the coming rainy season.
Even roofs which are hardly a year old need some repairing.
So with the idea of avoiding in future any loss of time on
such work, I form the plan of gradually replacing all leaf-
tile roofs with corrugated iron. The former have to be
renewed every three years and need continual attention.
In the course of a few years one spends as much on them
as if corrugated iron had been used at first, and one has
the trouble into the bargain of collecting the stitched leaves.
What hours Dr. Nessmann spent in palavering about the
leaf-tiles for the roof of our dwelling-house! What a number of crews we had to supply with food and presents in
order to get the material here! So I proceed to order in
Europe several hundred square yards of corrugated iron,
although I am not sure that I have the means to pay for
them.

In the middle of September we get our first rains, and
the cry is to bring all building timber under cover. As we
have in the hospital hardly a man capable of work, I begin,
assisted by two loyal helpers, to haul beams and planks
about myself. Suddenly I catch sight of a negro in a white
suit sitting by a patient whom he has come to visit. "Hullo,
friend!" I call out, "won't you lend us a hand?" "I am
an intellectual and don't drag wood about," came the
answer. "You're lucky," I reply. "I, too, wanted to
become an intellectual, but I didn't succeed."

CHAPTER VI

Autumn, 1925

Now the famine has reached us, too. It has, in fact, been here since the beginning of the summer, but its presence was concealed by the importation of rice from Europe. That has stopped for a time, and the famine is at once evident.

There are several circumstances to blame for this disastrous shortage of rice. First and foremost, the traders here estimated far too low the deficit in bananas and manioc root which inevitably resulted from the failure to plant what was needed last year. So from the very first they were ordering too little rice. Secondly, a ship bringing several thousand tons of rice for our west coast was wrecked, the cargo getting soaked and ruined. Other ships, loaded with rice, lost, so it was announced, a great deal of time while discharging their cargoes, through unfavourable weather in our bad African roadsteads. So it will be some weeks before we get anything from them, and it will take months to make good the serious shortage. The panic that is setting in, and the accompanying storm of demands for the precious commodity only make the matter worse.

Worse off than any others are the small timber-merchants, who have always relied on regular monthly deliveries, and who at their far-away outposts only learnt of the disaster when it was already upon us.

For the present, however, the feeding of the sick in our hospital is provided for. In June and July when the first signs of the shortage appeared and we also expected a rise in price, we laid in an emergency stock of over 5,000 lb., so as to be prepared for all contingencies. In reliance on the loyalty of our friends in Europe we ventured on this huge purchase, though without the extra rooms provided by the new house I could not dream of piling up such a supply. Nor without the motor-boat could I have got it transported with the requisite speed, for as soon as rice is brought it must be taken away at once, or it runs the risk of being disposed of at other places to our disadvantage. With our big reserve, for which we are envied on all sides, we can, so long as it lasts, keep our heads fairly well above water. Yet as soon as ever we hear in the distance the siren of any steamer, big or little, off I go with the motor-boat into the big channel where the factories are, so as not to be overlooked in the distribution of any rice that may have arrived. Very often, however, the steamer brings every conceivable thing except rice!

The number of sick who have to be housed and fed now amounts to about 125. Then there is the hospital staff. From 130 to 175 lb. of rice has to be dealt out every day, if not more. Several times we have found ourselves with just enough for a few days only, but on each occasion I have succeeded at the last moment in unearthing a supply somewhere, and for that my hearty thanks before all to the motor-boat!

How the hospital could be broken up and its inmates dispersed, if our supplies actually gave out, I cannot imagine. Many patients are sixty or ninety miles from home, some even farther, and I see no means of getting them there. It is hard enough in ordinary times to get the cured away as quickly as we should like. Many of them have to stay on and be a burden on our stores for eight or ten days, till a canoe or motor-boat turns up which is going to their districts. Nor are they at all anxious to leave us; elsewhere hunger is lying in wait for them.

Things look bad at the timber-sites, work on most of them being at a standstill. The Bendjabis range the forest trying to support life with berries, fungi, roots, wild honey, palm-nuts, and pineapples, which last grow wild here. Sometimes a gang of them stumbles on an old manioc plantation in which they can still dig up some tubers. At the end of November the mango trees are in fruit, and can be found wherever there has been a village. In December, maize sown in the first days of September is ready for cutting. Bananas cannot be reckoned on before February.

It is refreshing to see how the timber-merchants help each other. Many a one of them who has managed to get some sacks of rice gives some to his neighbour, although he is a trade rival. I myself give a little help to the mission at Samkita, to two friendly merchants, and to an English factory.

Now that rice is the only available food, I get, unfortunately, ample confirmation of my experience that an exclusive diet of rice favours the appearance of dysentery among the natives of this country. There are at the present time dozens of walking skeletons among the population of our hospital.

In the middle of October Mlle Emma Hausknecht joins us as second nurse. She was a teacher in Alsace, and I have known her a long time; she promised years ago to come and help me some day. She now undertakes the housekeeping and the care of the white patients, setting Nurse Kottmann free for the hospital below.

What a relief it is for us that there is now someone who can have an eye on the patients and at the same time keep things straight everywhere! We ourselves are hardly able to stir all day from the consulting-room and the dispensary. Now it is possible to ensure that the dysentery patients get their soup and have their places cleaned. Now there is someone to see that the sick have what they need. All disputes which occur in the hospital are now brought to Nurse Kottmann and are decided by her. She superintends every day the distribution of the food-rations, a business which hitherto has been left only too often to Dominic. She takes care that a fire is kept going under our store of dried fish, so that it may not go bad nor get infected with maggots. Every morning, too, she gives out spades, axes, and bush-knives for the work of the day, and counts them at night to make sure that they have all been returned. She also exercises supervision over the canoes. She has all the linen and the material for dressings under her care, and arranges who shall do the washing. When there are operations, she is the operation sister.

To find order and system thus gradually coming into the working of the hospital would give us all new courage for our work, if the situation brought about by our want of more space, by dysentery, and by famine were not so disrupting. And it gets worse every day. The infection with dysentery germs gets worse and worse; almost every day someone is discovered who has caught the infection here, and fresh cases are continually being brought in. Not long ago a single morning brought us six at once.

This epidemic of dysentery makes me realise how detrimental it is to the work of the hospital that the site on which it stands is too small. If it were possible for us to erect isolation wards at a convenient distance from the rest of our buildings, and so keep the dysentery patients separated from the others, my hospital would not be so infected as it is with dysentery germs. The mission, however willing, cannot afford to place any more ground at my disposal, because if they did, the hospital buildings would soon be too near the schools and the houses of the mission families. To extend our buildings in any other direction than towards the mission is an impossibility, since in every other is either steeply rising ground, or a swamp, or the river.

How I regret now that when I came back I had not the courage to rebuild the hospital on another larger site, instead of staying on the old one in order to make use of the old buildings, and not be compelled to start clearing a new site for new ones. And yet, without workers, without canoes, without building materials, how could I have ventured on the task of building the hospital all over again on a site which would first have to be cleared and levelled?

Again because I have not room enough, I cannot do what I ought for the poor mentally afflicted. The cell which I have for them, a dark den without a window, stands among the buildings which house the sick. I have no lock-up room which gets air and sunlight. Noisy mental patients I cannot take in for long periods, because the other patients cannot stand the noise so near. I therefore have to send them back in bonds to their village, where they will very likely be tormented to death, whereas under my care they might be cured. What I suffer at heart in such a case I have never let even my helpers know. If I only had a larger building site, I could house the mental patients at a distance from the others and carry out my duty to them as well.

But, anyhow, the area of my hospital is too small. It could hold the buildings needed for fifty patients, which was about the number during my first period of residence. But with the patients numbering permanently about 120 it is far too small. The activities of three doctors are carried on in two rooms, each about thirteen feet square, with two small side-rooms, one of which serves as the dispensary, while the other is at once laboratory and sterilisation room. In the room in which we examine the patients, Joseph makes the injections, two natives roll bandages, and two others wash bottles. There is a pushing and jostling as at a fair. We try in vain to get rid of the conviction that our work is seriously spoilt by these conditions with the fatigue and nervous strain that inevitably accompany them.

In the wards this want of space is distressing, even apart from the worry of the dysentery. We cannot put the dying by themselves; we have not even a separate place for the dead; they have to stay in the ward till they are carried out to the cemetery.

Nor can we house our staff properly; with the exception of Joseph and Aloys, the cook, they occupy odd corners and sheds. To keep them with us I promise that I will some day have them housed as befits human beings, but how that is to be done is a puzzle even to myself. If I could house all my workers properly, I should be able, in spite of the work being far from light, to get all the needed orderlies, the lack of whom hinders us so seriously in our work.

Then, again, the danger of fire is so great that we dare not deceive ourselves by ignoring it. Our sick-wards and all our buildings are so huddled together that if a fire did break out, they would all go up hopelessly in flames together.

Shall I, then, be angry with the dysentery, which so pitilessly drives me up against the insufficiency of my site and of my buildings?

The famine, for its part, does its share by warning me that it is an unsound and dangerous position when an undertaking like mine does not stand on its own ground, and is not surrounded by a piece of land on which it can produce some of its food supply. If at the beginning of summer I had been able to plant some maize, I should now have some help with the feeding of my patients.

There are almost always in my hospital from twenty to thirty people who are capable of light work on the land. First of all come the attendants who accompany the patients, and whom I have to feed in any case. Why should they sit there all day idle? That by such work they should to some extent pay for their own food and that of their sick companions is only fair and just. Then come a certain number of light and convalescent cases whom a little work will not hurt. Patients with ulcers on their feet whose skin is already granulating have often so little discomfort that they can quite reasonably be employed for a few hours. So I have a lot of labour power in my hospital, but it is unused because the hospital has no land.

It is only recently that this consideration has become weighty; when there were only forty patients, the employable labour power meant much less than it does with 120 or more. Nor had the idea of burdening oneself with farm work near the hospital anything attractive, so long as one could somehow manage to procure bananas and manioc. Now, however, when famine is raging, and it is becoming more and more evident that it is likely to prove a standing source of difficulty everywhere, I cannot but see that the hospital, if it is to continue its existence, must itself provide part at least of its own food.

On these and similar thoughts I ponder during these dismal weeks, and in the course of October my ponderings

take shape in a resolution to remove the hospital to a bigger
site, which will be its own property, and that as soon as
possible. I already have the corrugated iron for the roofs.
It was to have roofed the wards of the old hospital; now
it will perform the same service in the new one. Nor shall
I be short of labour, for he who has rice can always have
labour. How subdued is the temper of our inmates to-day
compared with what it was in the old days! They no
longer try to evade the labour tasks, but even offer for them,
because those who work get more to eat than the rest.

The decision thus arrived at I carry about with me without a word to anyone. I make solitary journeys to visit the
piece of land which alone is worth considering for a site.
It is three kilometres (one and three-quarter miles) upstream from here, on the same bank, and just at the point
where the Ogowe divides into two branches. Once some
big villages stood there, and N'Kombe, the "Sun-king"
—for there were sun-kings in Africa too!—himself lived
there. The spot was, therefore, once cultivated here and
there, so that the forest which now covers it is comparatively young, and the labour of clearing the site will be
correspondingly easy. Moreover, since there were once
dwellings and plantations, there are oil-palms everywhere.
A spacious valley not far from the river provides a good
site for the hospital, and the gently rising hills just above
it look as if formed to take our dwelling-houses.

I had been at the place many times, for M. Morel had
drawn my attention to it during my first residence here.
So the day after my return I revisited it, and regretted not
being in a position to let the hospital rise again there in
a new form, instead of my settling down amid the ruins
of the old one. Now I come again, under the compulsion
of dysentery and famine, to settle here after all.

My application for a grant of the land is met by the
District Commissioner in the most friendly way. The for-
malities to be gone through will take months, but in consideration of the special circumstances and of the fact
that no objections are likely to be raised, the site is put at
my disposal provisionally, I am given about seventy hec-

tares (172 acres) as a "concession." This means that the land remains the property of the State, but is handed over to me to be built on or cultivated, whatever we build and whatever improvements we make remaining our own property. This is the only system of land-ownership in the colony.

On returning from my visit to the District Commissioner I call the doctors and nurses together and disclose to them what is under way. At first they are dumb with astonishment; then they break out into shouts of joy. There is no need to convince them of the necessity of the move; they have been for a long time even more convinced than I myself. Only we all wonder alike how we shall find the courage to face such an undertaking. The natives stare at us with astonishment; to such gesticulation and such a din of conversation among us they are quite unaccustomed!

I, however, think of the sacrifice it means for my wife and daughter. They expect to see me back at the end of this winter (1925-6); as it is, I can scarcely hope to get to Europe before the beginning of the following one. The building cannot be done without my superintendence, and for the laying out of the hospital use must be made of my experience. Once the roofs are on the buildings, others can undertake the internal arrangements.

CHAPTER VII

Autumn and Winter, 1925-6

THE first thing we have to do is to peg out the area provisionally granted to us, so as to be able to make the ground plan which has to be handed in to the District Commissioner. Compass in hand, we work our way into the forest and cut tracks which make measurement possible. If we come upon a swamp, we have to content ourselves with driving long poles into the soft ground at intervals of 20 metres. If we stumble on a thicket inhabited by the formidable red ants, white men and black all try who can retreat the quickest. These ants establish themselves on the branches, and drop in clusters on invaders of their preserve.

While the pegging out is being done, the work of clearing the ground is also commenced, for we must as soon as possible have a piece of land ready for cultivation in order to sow some maize. Since it will be necessary for a longish time, so far as we can see, to feed our inmates with rice from Europe, it is a matter of giving them, in addition, some food containing vitamins.

For the deforesting everyone in the hospital who can move hand and foot is summoned each morning, provided with axe and bush-knife, and taken by canoe about two miles upstream to our new estate. This troop is composed of men and women who are staying with us as companions of the patients. There are in it also some patients who are now well again and stay to help us out of gratitude. All are willing, because those who work get a whole food-ration, while the ordinary hospital inmate, with the exception of those who are seriously ill, gets only two-thirds. There are periods, however, when even the workers have to be rationed sparingly, for the famine continues as bad as ever.

The workers get not only their food but a present as well. If I were to ask them what they would like for their present they would one and all ask for tobacco and some alcoholic drink. When the slave trade flourished in these parts tobacco and alcohol, together with gunpowder and lead, represented the highest current values, and they have kept this position down to to-day. It is only with difficulty that these people are getting accustomed to receive their presents from me in a different form. I give only useful things : spoons—forks are hardly ever wanted —cups, plates, knives, cooking-pots, sleeping mats of raphia, blankets, material for clothes, and mosquito nets.

It is no easy job to collect the people each morning for the journey. Dr. Nessmann and Dr. Lauterburg know something about that. Every day they have to shout themselves hoarse till at last the canoes are full. The native orderlies cannot help in this, since they have not authority enough, nor can they decide who is fit for work and who is not.

If we have plenty of workers, the canoes are not sufficient, and the women have to travel in the motor-boat. There is then such a chattering that the noise of the motor stands out against it much as a harmonium would if played against a full orchestra.

We get, as a rule, about fifteen workers, which in view of the overwhelming amount that has to be done is far too few. And to ensure that some progress is made one of us must go with them as supervisor; left to themselves they would hardly do anything. Why should they, who happen to be here just now, exert themselves so that others, who will be in the hospital a few months hence, may have maize to eat, and even be housed in good wards !

A day with these people moves on like a symphony. Lento : They take very grumpily the axes and bush-knives that I distribute to them on landing. In snail-tempo the procession goes to the spot where bush and tree are to be cut down. At last everyone is in his place. With great caution the first blows are struck.

Moderato: Axes and bush-knives move in extremely moderate time, which the conductor tries in vain to quicken. The midday break puts an end to the tedious movement.

Adagio: With much trouble I have brought the people back to the work place in the stifling forest. Not a breath of wind is stirring. One hears from time to time the strokes of an axe.

Scherzo: A few jokes, to which in my despair I tune myself up, are successful. The mental atmosphere gets livelier, merry words fly here and there, and a few begin to sing. It is now getting a little cooler, too. A tiny gust of wind steals up from the river into the thick undergrowth.

Finale: All are jolly now. The wicked forest, on account of which they have to stand here instead of sitting comfortably in the hospital, shall have a bad time of it. Wild imprecations are hurled at it. Howling and yelling they attack it, axes and bush-knives vie with each other in battering it. But—no bird must fly up, no squirrel show itself, no question must be asked, no command given. With the very slightest distraction the spell would be broken. Then the axes and knives would come to rest, everybody would begin talking about what had happened or what they had heard, and there would be no getting them again into train for work.

Happily, no distraction comes. The music gets louder and faster. If this finale lasts even a good half-hour the day has not been wasted. And it continues till I shout "Amani! Amani" (Enough! Enough!), and put an end to work for the day.

The sun is still well up in the sky. But the walk from the work-place to the river, the return in the canoes, the collecting of the tools and the paddles, and the distribution of the food-ration takes nearly an hour and a half. And at the Equator darkness sets in just after 6 o'clock. To superintend the delivery of the axes and knives and the distribution of the rations by lantern light is extraordinarily exhausting. Moreover, doctors and nurses are, as far as possible, to cease all outside work when darkness falls, that they may not get bitten by mosquitoes and so risk getting an attack of malaria.

Whoever is with the workers must, in the afternoon, continually watch the sky to see that no thunderstorm is threatening. As soon as he sees any suspicious-looking clouds, he must give the signal for return. The men must not be allowed to get wet, because that often brings on attacks of malaria. Nor must they be surprised by a storm on the river. Many of them come, of course, from the interior and cannot swim. If the canoes were to upset, they would be lost.

On December 4th the canoes are surprised on their return journey by a terrible thunderstorm. Dr. Nessmann, who was in charge that day, had not noticed the danger in time. We wait for an hour and a half in dreadful anxiety, but at last the storm abates. One after the other the canoes arrive in pitch darkness and under a deluge of rain. They had had just time to reach the bank somewhere or other, and no one was drowned. I mount to the doctor's house, almost dizzy with joy.

On that portion of the new site where the buildings are to stand, we leave some trees standing to provide shade. Where we want to plant, every tree must be sacrificed, oil-palms alone being spared. Big hardwood trees give us great trouble. Several men must work for several days before one of the giants comes down, and then it takes days longer to cut it up.

The simplest plan would be to leave where it falls everything that is felled, and then in the dry season to burn it, as the natives do when they lay out a new plantation. We act differently since we shall be glad later on to be spared the labour of hauling from a distance all the wood that the hospital needs for fuel. The logs are therefore built up into big piles on the spot, the trunks being left as they are. The tremendous roots, too, are left in the ground. What toil it would be to dig them out! But we shall sow between the trunks and the roots. To

turn the forest into good arable land is a work of genera-
tions.

The piles of logs provide, unfortunately, a good home for
snakes, but we acquiesce in the inconvenience as part of
the bargain. There are so many in our grounds anyhow
that a few hundred more make little difference. Every
day as we clear further we despatch some, among them
some of the most dangerous kinds.

Everywhere in the undergrowth we come across oil-
palms, which can neither flower nor fruit, because the
matted vines lie upon them like a thick carpet. We often
have to cut a tunnel through this undergrowth to work
our way to the foot of the palms. We cut the climbing
plants through near the root, and then leave them to get
dry and to rot; only then can we drag them down from
the trees, and even then we have more than enough trouble
with them. It takes on the average about a week to free
a group of oil-palms from the carpet which covers them.
How thankful the palms are when the sun can at last shine
upon them!

There is always going on in the primeval forest, though
without a sound to betray it, an uncanny struggle between
creepers and trees. Anything which cannot work its way
up above the creeper-growth into the sunlight, dies a slow
and painful death.

The oil-palm is not a native of the primeval forest. It
is only to be found on the outskirts of villages, or in places
near which there once were villages. It has been spared
by the action of birds and monkeys, who carry off into
the forest the fruit of the trees growing near the huts,
and after consuming the fibrous, oil-containing husk, let
the nut, with its kernel, fall to the ground, where the
latter takes root and grows.

So after getting rid of the other vegetation we find in
many spots whole groves of oil-palms, which are valuable
as a help in the feeding of our sick. In the course of years
we shall be able to give the natives a good portion of their
fat ration in the form of palm oil. We prepare it from

the husk of the nut. It is well known that the red nuts—
in shape and size like walnuts—grow in several dozens
together on a common receptacle, the whole forming a
big cluster. Oil is got both from the fibrous husk which
encloses the nut, the so-called fruit flesh, and from the
hard kernel which is inside the very hard nut. To get the
oil from the kernels strong presses are needed, so the oil
is not prepared in Africa, but these " palm kernels " are
shipped to Europe, where they are manufactured into oils
and vegetable fats of the most varied sort. When we have
procured our oil from the fibrous husk, the nuts are shelled,
and the kernels are exchanged for rice at a store. The
nut-cracking is the job of patients suffering from ulcers
on their feet and capable of no other work.

In the hospital we are still hard worked, for the dysentery
epidemic continues, and we sometimes get half a dozen
new cases in a single morning. Many of these poor creatures
are mere skeletons, doomed irretrievably to death. Often-
times there are not people enough in the hospital to dig
the graves and carry out the bodies to the cemetery, and
then we ourselves have to work as sextons and bearers.

And again and again it happens that patients who come
with other diseases get infected. Menzoghe, a poor woman,
who by her own wish had her arm with badly infected
wounds taken off, catches it and dies. Similar is the fate
of a poor sick man, deserted by his family, whom I brought
to the hospital when I was on a journey upstream to save
him from dying of hunger. And these are not the only
victims whom we lose in this tragic fashion ! At times I
am so depressed that I can hardly summon up energy
enough to work. I should like best to send away, till the
epidemic is over, all the people who come for an operation.
But they will not be turned away.

In November we operate on an elephantiasis tumour
weighing more than 40 kilos (88 lb.), the operation lasting
from 10.30 to 4 p.m. For these cases there is no
need, fortunately, to use a general anæsthetic. When Dr.
Lauterburg, after the operation, proceeded to carry the

patient to his berth, an old negro danced solemnly along in front of him. He knew of no better way in which to express his feelings. King David, no doubt, felt much the same way when he danced before the Ark of the Covenant. Then all the hospital inmates crowded round the patient's berth, while he himself seized the doctor's hands and never wearied of stroking them and ejaculating, "Akewa! Akewa!" (Thank you! Thank you!).

About this time we operated on several smaller tumours, weighing only 10 to 20 kilos.

There are also a number of hernia cases. Everyone who gets relief from his sufferings sends us hernia patients from his home district.

But of the strangulated hernias we really get fewer cases now than when I was here before. That does not mean that there are fewer cases. But since nearly all the men are now at work getting timber and in the swamps far from their villages, there are often not enough people in the village to paddle at once to us the poor man whose hernia has got strangulated. So instead of finding deliverance with us, he dies a torturing death in his hut.

Accidents are continually giving us surgical work. Our worst case is that of a native, called Mefane, who had both his legs shattered below the knee by a gun shot at very short range. He was sheltering for the night beneath the house, built on piles, of a European without the latter's knowledge, and he was hit by the charge from a gun which was accidentally fired through the floor. In this case again methyl-violet proved its value. We first removed the splinters of bone, and then by plugging and padding the wound with strips of gauze dipped in a solution of pyoktanin and kept moist, we succeeded in mastering the suppuration. But it will be a long time before the ends of the shattered bones reunite again.

While the man is under treatment two of his relatives have to stay in the hospital to carry him to the operating-room for his dressings to be changed, and to help us in our various undertakings. Being in urgent need of workers, we always try to arrange that surgical patients who have relatives shall be accompanied by two attendants who are capable of manual work and who, from the day of the operation till the patient is discharged, shall help in the clearing of the new site in return for food and presents. We often do manage this, but cannot insist on it too decidedly. The result might be that, to escape having to work for us, relatives would abstain from bringing sufferers who ought to be operated upon. With the natives one cannot adhere rigidly to principles; one must always act with due consideration for all circumstances which ought to be taken into account.

Towards Christmas our little rooms for white patients get filled up. The case which causes us most anxiety is that of M. Stähli, a Swiss, who came to us with a row of deep-seated abscesses and a severe sunstroke. We do everything we can for him, but without much hope; he lies in a state of almost unbroken coma. On Christmas Eve we bring him a little tree decked with candles and sing carols at his bedside. He has a clear moment or two and understands what it means, a happy smile lighting up his thin, yellow face.

That very evening there is great excitement among the patients. A maniac is secretly deposited here, and causes universal confusion.

In the afternoon of Christmas Day our Swiss patient dies. As the burial must take place next morning—a body cannot be kept above ground in the tropics—the coffin has to be taken in hand at once.

CHAPTER VIII

1926

FROM the beginning of 1926 I have to be on the new site almost every day. While Mlle Kottmann leads the clearing party, I undertake with another team the work on the actual building site.

How are we to build? We are unanimous on one point —that we will not have in the new hospital any bamboo huts or any leaf roofs. These huts require constant repairs, and after every storm holes have to be mended in the roofs. The storm, that is, lifts the light leaf-tiles and pushes them together, so that uncovered spaces are left. And every three years the roof has to be replaced by a new one.

It often happened that the doctors could devote only the morning to the sick, and had to employ the afternoon on building repairs. So now that we are reconstructing the hospital we intend to have permanent buildings which will not require constant maintenance.

Buildings of stone or brick are unthinkable; they would cost us too much time, and far too much money. So we decide for wards of corrugated iron on a framework of hardwood. Hardwood it must be, since ordinary timbers would, in a few months, be the prey of termites.

These corrugated-iron wards we shall build on piles. Why? The hospital will spread out along the river, having to be built near it because the natives are accustomed to live near water. They like, too, to have their canoes within sight. The hospital will, indeed, stand on the slope of a hill a few metres above the normal high-water level, but we have to allow for exceptionally high floods. These might carry my buildings away if they stood on the ground itself; if they are on piles, the water flows away between the piles. Piles, therefore, on account of the river.

But also on account of the hill. For if two or three thunderstorms descend on us during the night, torrents of water rush down the hillside above us, and these would endanger my buildings if they stood on the ground itself; if they are on piles the water flows away between the piles.

So I shall be a modern prehistoric man, and build my hospital like a lake-dwellers' village, but of corrugated iron.

Learned men dispute whether the lake dwellings of our ancestors were built actually in the water or on the edge of it. On the whole the latter are doubtless right. When primitive man intends to make a permanent settlement near water or on a hillside, he is obliged to help himself out with piles. Piles safeguard him from danger caused by the water, and relieve him, a very important matter, of the toil of levelling a site. The road from the hut to the stone building leads over the pile dwelling.

Next there comes for us the question of getting the piles. The most suitable material is a special kind of hardwood which is somewhat rare. One of my black friends is kind enough to tell me of a spot higher up the river where there are groups of such trees not too far from the water. It must be upstream, because in canoes with a heavy load of timber we can only travel downstream. And only trees standing near water can be considered, because we cannot haul the heavy timber any but short distances over land or through swamps.

Dr. Nessmann is given the duty of fetching the piles. If we were to send the natives by themselves, they would come home with only a few poles in the boat.

The place indicated is about sixteen miles away on a mountain stream, which has rapids in it and is only navigable when the water is high. So Dr. Nessmann will be getting piles till spring comes. He made his first journey on January 4th, 1926, and returned a few days later with thirty piles. To secure the needed number the expedition will have to be repeated several times.

Meanwhile, to provide fuel, I get palm branches cut and piled in layers to dry. For it is necessary to char the piles in order to make them last longer, and this work I must superintend. Left to themselves the natives would either burn them altogether, or not char them sufficiently, and they would never have more than three or four piles in the fire. My plan is to throw up a broad bank of earth on which twenty already barked piles are so laid that one end projects as far as possible beyond the bank into the fire, which is kept burning the whole length of the bank. When this free end is sufficiently charred, the fire is allowed to go out and the pile is reversed, so that what rested before on the bank becomes the free end and rests on the fire. Thus the pile gets charred from end to end. The charring is made especially effective if water is poured over the glowing end before it is taken from the fire. If everything goes well, I can char from twenty to thirty piles a day.

By February 15th the store hut is erected and roofed with corrugated iron, with a room inside it which can be locked, for the tools used by those who work at the felling and the digging. Now we need no longer waste time at the start from the hospital over giving out axes, bush-knives, pickaxes, bill-hooks, and spades, nor in the evening go through the wearisome task of calling in, counting, and storing away all the tools in the darkness.

The store hut erected, we proceed at once to the driving of the piles for the first sick-ward. The important thing is that the hole for the pile shall have a strong and well-stamped-in layer of stones at the bottom for a foundation which will not give way. If a pile sinks with the weight of the house, the building, of course, comes out of the perpendicular.

Moreover, in fixing the piles care must be taken that they stand exactly in line, and that their top surfaces are exactly level. If they are not, the fixing of the beams upon them is very troublesome, for some have to be wedged up, others to have a piece cut away, according as a pile is too low or too high.

I set the piles fairly close to one another. Measured from centre to centre the distance is about $1\frac{1}{2}$ metres (4 feet 9 inches), so that four, five, or six rows are needed, according to the width of the building. With the piles so close together the beams that are to rest upon them need be of 10 to 15 centimetres only (4 to 6 inches) instead of 8.

The ward we begin with is 25 metres (about 80 feet) long and 5 wide. It is to contain two rooms for surgical patients, and a few small ones for the native orderlies. How it weighs on me that in the old hospital they have to live in holes and corners. They are now to have rooms with wooden floors and mosquito-proof netting. The pleasantness of their quarters will induce them to stay with me, even if the work is hard and the pay not high.

I am in a hurry to get this first building roofed. It will let me house Monenzalie, the black carpenter, and his helpers, and also some of those who work on the new site. That will mean two more hours a day secured for work, hours spent hitherto in journeys out and back.

At the end of February Dr. Nessmann is to return home in order to perform his military service, and on the 22nd Dr. Trensz, who is to take his place, arrives; he also is the son of a pastor in Alsace. He has scarcely unpacked, when he is taken by Dr. Nessmann on the last journey the latter will make for pile-getting. He has to learn the business, for it will now fall to his share.

I try sometimes leaving the building workers to themselves for an afternoon, or even for a whole day, because I so urgently need time for letters, for making out orders for goods, and for getting into touch again with the working of the hospital. But each time I have to regret it. If I am not there, either nothing is done or the work is done in such a way that it has to be done over again. On one such afternoon a carpenter sawed twenty valuable beams by wrong measurements.

I have written to Europe asking them to find me in either Alsace or Switzerland a young carpenter, to be sent out as quickly as possible for the beginning of the dry season.

And now there is some building work needed in the old hospital. For in March an insane patient who had been brought to me fastened in some stocks, tears down the cell made for the mental patients and breaks out of it, spread-

ing terror everywhere in the hospital. With a heavy heart
I have to give him back to the people who brought him.

Amid all the work and anxiety caused me by the new
hospital, there is one thing that comforts me, viz., that I
shall have there safe rooms for several mental patients,
and shall not have to turn any away because I have not
enough cells, or only cells which are not strong enough.
But in order to be able in the meanwhile to take at least
one or two sufferers, I rebuild the cell that has been ruined.
It now has two doors—a solid inner one and an outer one
with openings in it. If the patient is comparatively quiet,
he need not sit in darkness; the inner door is left open, and
through the openings he gets light and air with a view over
the landing-place and the river. The cell is only just ready
when there comes an inmate for it. How glad I am that
I did not shirk this temporary work, but did, in defiance
of the parable, put a piece of new cloth on the old garment.

While the carpenters are working on the first building,
I set the piles for those which are to follow, this difficult
work taking weeks. Often I have to push or to turn the
heavy pile just a centimetre or two so as to get into the
the right position, and while this is being done I cannot let
a native touch it. They cannot judge any movement, and
would push it or turn it right out of place. There is nothing
for it but to get into the pit myself, put my arms round
it, and move it as required. If all goes well, I can get a
dozen piles into position in a day.

The new hospital is becoming a regular village. It is
to provide accommodation for 200 patients and their attendants. In the part which stands farthest downstream it will
consist of three parallel lines of buildings. At the upper
end of these lines there will be only two, so that the big
building in which the doctors carry on their work shall
have an empty space in front of it and get some breeze
from the river.

Every building has its central line running east and west,
so that the sun rises and sets opposite the gable ends, and
never strikes the side walls. For we are close to the Equator,
and the sun travels very little towards north or south.

Hence the side walls of a building so oriented and provided with a projecting roof only catch the sun about Christmas and midsummer. The building is therefore considerably cooler than one built north and south, on the walls of which the sun's rays would rest every morning and evening. These building rules should be much more observed and followed in the tropics than they usually are.

I also purposely make these buildings long and narrow, the form which the sun can injuriously affect least. The problem also of light and air, a problem which is so important with tropical buildings when there is a projecting roof, is easier to solve with narrow buildings than with wide ones. And so in my buildings the rooms are not side by side, but end to end.

In the course of the spring I have fixed the piles for the entire hospital village. Besides the building measuring 27 yards by $5\frac{1}{2}$, which is now approaching completion, there will be four others with dimensions of $14\frac{1}{2}$ yards by $7\frac{1}{2}$, 28 yards by $7\frac{1}{2}$, 39 yards by 5, and 24 yards by 9.

Simultaneously with the buildings for the black patients, I begin a house for the white ones. It will be higher up the river than the main block of buildings, and will be 24 yards by 9, supported by forty-eight piles.

On April 26th Hans Muggensturm arrives, a young Swiss from St. Gallen, and now I can breathe, though not quite freely. The great question is whether he can get on with the natives. If he has not that gift, his work will be much less valuable than it might be. But in a few days it is clear that he has it.

And what is the gift? It consists in being able to combine in right measure firmness and kindness, to avoid unnecessary talk, and to find a jocular remark at the right moment.

So now the new European helper takes over the superintendence of the three carpenters and their labourers, and I can devote myself to the fixing of the piles, the preparation of the sites, and the collecting of the materials. My first duty now is to see that the various kinds of work fit into one another, and that timber and iron, screws and nails, are always at hand when wanted.

Now I can undertake the necessary journeys to get timber without the building work coming to a stop. For time is precious. In the dry season—from the end of May to the middle of September—the most important buildings must be roofed. In the autumn, when the rainy season begins, we shall work at the partitions and the fittings.

During the dry season, too, we shall begin digging a well down by the hospital, and in the autumn I shall fix the piles for our dwelling-house on the hill above; 105 piles for a house 33 yards by 9.

The garden, upstream from the hospital, which we laid out and sowed in spring, now gives us beans and cabbages. Unfortunately, its lower part was reached by the exceptionally early autumn flood, and we lost part of the crop.

In the early months of the year the work for the patients is so heavy that the two doctors can hardly get through it, for we always have from 120 to 160 black patients on our hands. Speaking generally, we can say they suffer from malaria, framboesia, dysentery, leprosy, and sleeping-sickness, but nearly a third of them are, as usual, with us on account of the phagedenic ulcers. From fifteen to twenty berths are occupied by patients who have had, or who are waiting for, an operation.

Accidents bring us just now a lot of surgical work. One man falls from a high tree on which he was getting honey, and is brought here with a serious fracture. Another is cutting down a tree on which he believes there is honey, so as to secure the tasty spoil in comfort, and the tree falls upon a hut and kills an unfortunate woman. From a timber-site we receive a man who had got caught under a rolling tree-trunk. In spite of his severe injuries we cure him.

A longish time is spent with us by a native hunter, whose hand has been torn by a gorilla with its terrible teeth. He shot at the creature, which encountered him unexpectedly on the forest path, and thought himself lucky that it retired instead of rushing at him. But it lay in wait behind a tree to catch him when he came back, and there was a struggle in which the hunter had a hair's-breadth escape from death.

Another native's encounter with an elephant had a less happy ending. The elephant came to a spot near Samkita, where mahogany was being felled, but on seeing the men there made a leisurely retreat. The men determined to bring him down by their traditional method of sneaking after him and cutting the Achilles tendons of his hind legs, the crafty way in which in earlier times thousands of elephants in the forests of Central Africa had been rendered helpless and then cruelly done to death. But the Samkita negroes have not the skill of their forefathers; the elephant noticed the coming onslaught and charged. The nearest native he threw into the air, and then, having bored him through with his tusks, he quietly trotted off. The man's injuries were so severe that we could not save his life.

The primeval forest also witnesses accidents caused by careless shooting. One morning we received a native whom, while he was digging for roots in the bush, another had taken for a wild boar and had shot in the back. The unhappy shooter, N'Zigge by name, accompanies his victim, whose wound proves a fatal one. Immediately after his death N'Zigge sends for his wife and child to come as soon as possible, and I keep them all in the hospital because their lives are now unsafe. I accompany N'Zigge also to the District Commissioner's, where the case is dealt with, lest he should be murdered on the way. As it is only a case of homicide through negligence, his sentence is only to pay a considerable sum of money to the family of the dead man, and give them a goat as well, the latter in obedience to the rule that when a life has been lost something living must be given as part of the compensation. In order to be safe and to earn the money, N'Zigge, who is a pleasant, quiet fellow, remains with his family here, and helps in the tree-felling. He becomes in time our best and most loyal worker.

Once we have brought to us all at once half a dozen injured men, victims of a fight which took place on a timber-site between the workers.

On another occasion we receive two natives in a terrible condition, because on a road-making job about ninety miles to the south they had been blasting stone with dynamite and had not taken shelter quickly enough. One dies a few days after his arrival, the other is saved.

At the beginning of the year we receive several mental cases, many of them, however, with merely temporary derangements, due to sleeping-sickness or to poisons which cause nervous excitement. One of the former, N'Tsama by name, was reduced to a skeleton. We treat him with tryparsamid, the new sleeping-sickness drug from the Rockefeller Institute, which we have just received for experimental purposes. N'Tsama's excitement slowly disappears, but his mental disturbance remains in the form of an uncanny kleptomania which exposes the poor fellow to unpleasantly rough treatment from the hospital inmates who suffer thereby. Having also, like many sleeping-sickness patients, an abnormal appetite, he coaxes to him my poultry, so as to make them a contribution to his cooking-pot, and many a one falls a victim to his wiles. Then, like so many other patients, N'Tsama catches dysentery and hovers for two months between life and death, so weak that he has to be fed by others. At last, as spring approaches, he gets over the dysentery, and the treatment with tryparsamid can be resumed. Then the kleptomania slowly disappears, and, having become strong enough to walk about, he stands nearly all day on the river bank and fishes, though without catching much. One day, when there were planks to be unloaded and taken up to the hospital, I laughingly called to N'Tsama to leave his fishing and help us, whereupon he lifted up a plank and carried it away on his head. There is much jubilation over this in the hospital, because it is thus evident to all that even sleeping-sickness sufferers in the last stage of the disease, who have hitherto been doomed to death, can now be restored to healthy life. At the beginning of the summer N'Tsama asks to be allowed to help with the forest clearing, and he stays with us as a labourer. "The Doctor is my father (he says) and the hospital is my village." The only relic of the sleeping-sickness is a proneness to fatigue and irritation. On account of this he is only allowed to work when one of us is present, so that too much exertion may not be expected from him, and that the others may not excite him by making fun of him. Since then we have had many excellent results from the use of this drug.

" Bayer 205 " (called also Germanin), the drug produced by the Bavarian Dye Company, constitutes, with the American tryparsamid, a great advance in the fight with sleeping-sickness. Each of them has its own advantages and disadvantages. Tryparsamid is more effective in advanced cases than Bayer 205, but has the disadvantage that, like the atoxyl we used to employ, it often damages the optic nerve and may result in blindness. In spite of all our caution we, too, have one case of blindness to register.

With how much more confidence than hitherto we now hold our position in the fight against sleeping-sickness ! We have had this month to diagnose three Europeans as in the early stage of the disease, but they were all saved. And they had no need to go to Europe to recruit; as soon as the cure was over, they could go straight back to work.

And what a number of natives get cured now, whom in past days we should have had to give up as hopeless cases because they had come to us in the last stage of the disease !

One day I have some business at the factories and see a native lying asleep at the side of the path. No one can tell me anything about him. " He has been lying here for a day, and is probably drunk," said the natives whom I questioned, and off they went their several ways. I put him into my boat and brought him to the hospital, where the microscope revealed that there in the hot sun his sleep was not that of the drunkard, but that of the victim of sleeping-sickness. When, some weeks later, he recovered his power of speech, we learnt that he was coming up from the coast, and wanted to go to his home in the interior.

We also get several poison cases one after the other. The native timber-merchant who told me where to find the piles for my new buildings notices that his quite intelligent son is beginning to stumble, and to sit staring stupidly in front of him. I at once suspect poison, so the boy is isolated, has to take powdered charcoal, and gets no food but what has been prepared under careful supervision. He slowly recovers. Probably someone was poisoning him to wreak his revenge on the father.

Another native timber-merchant whom I know is brought here in a strange condition. He seems to be fully conscious, but can neither speak nor swallow. His muscles show a remarkable rigidity, and his arms and legs tremble persistently, though only gently. He shows cataleptic symptoms, keeping his arms, for instance, in the position in which another person has placed them. He asks by signs for a pen, but is unable to write. As he spits all food out of his mouth, he is fed for weeks through the nose with a tube, and his cure depends on whether we can effectively overcome the tension of the muscles. He is treated with chloral hydrate, and intravenous injections of various drugs.

What trouble Dr. Trensz has with this man, the first case of poison that he has to deal with! He is well enough to be sent home at the end of three months, but has no recollection of what was done to him in the hospital.

This timber-merchant had shortly before had a dispute over money with some family connections who had a share in the business. These, then, will have been the persons who gave the poison, someone suggests. But one must not make such obvious inferences in Africa! To anyone familiar with native mentality it will seem probable that an enemy who had been planning against him for some time, or someone who wanted him out of the way, was using the quarrel as an opportunity for poisoning him, because he reckoned that suspicion would fall on the relatives who were engaged in the dispute.

What an uncanny place Equatorial Africa is with its many tragedies in which poison plays a part!

Frequently, however, the poisoning is unintentional. The sick man who seeks help from a medicine-man is given too much of the dangerous stuff in which the latter deals. Such a patient was brought to us this spring in a terrible condition. He could neither stand, nor speak, nor swallow, and it cost us endless toil and trouble to snatch him from death.

Simultaneously with him we had with us a medicine-man with a severe ulcer on his tongue. We found the causative organisms to be fusiform bacilli and spirochætes, such as are found also in the tropical phagedenic ulcers. We treated the medicine-man as we should a colleague, because our policy is to keep on good terms with all of them, so that they may send to us of their own accord the sufferers for whom their art can do nothing.

For the treatment of the phagedenic ulcers we have now, to guide us, our own tried method, which is much simpler than the usual one, and gives better results.

The latter consists in putting the patient under an anæsthetic, and then scraping his sore with the sharp-edged spoon, in order to remove all diseased tissue, after which it is covered with disinfecting compresses which are renewed daily. This is a very troublesome method. What a way of commencing treatment when five or six savages are to be put upon the table one after the other and anæsthetised! The method is also expensive, for ether and ethyl chloride, being inflammable commodities, have to travel on the ship's deck and pay a higher freight.

So our efforts have for some time been directed towards managing without an anæsthetic and scraping, especially since many of the natives, upset by the shriek that others made when the anæsthetising began, were afraid of being put to sleep, and preferred to have themselves taken home uncured rather than face the scraping. One evening we heard a patient, who had just gone through the anæsthetising and the scraping, say to his neighbour: "Yes, the doctor wanted to kill me. He put some poison into my nose, and I was actually dead. But he hadn't enough poison, and I came to life again!"

We began by substituting for the scraping of the sore a dabbing of its surface with a sublimate pastille, and this is repeated on several consecutive days. This made possible a very satisfactory removal of the diseased tissue, only this was very painful. We therefore tried whether we could

not do as well with a daily syringing. And it was successful! This new method allows us to avoid any touching
of the sore at all—even the gentlest is very painful, as I
know by experience—and yet at the same time to get the
antiseptic down through the thick layer of necrotic tissue
to the very base of the ulcer much better than before. The
pus is wiped off with a gauze swab, and all loose sloughs
are removed; but all rubbing or pressure is avoided, for
both are extremely painful. After this the ulcer is washed
out with sterile water, and irrigation treatment is instituted.
The fluid we use is a 1/6000 solution of mercury cyanide.
The ulcer is treated every morning, from five to twenty
minutes according to its size, with drops which fall, about
sixty to the minute, from a height of 50 to 75 cm. (20-30
inches). Drops from such a height cause at first acute
pain, so for the first few days the height is kept to a few
centimetres only; but the drops gradually make their way
through the thick superficial layer of necrotic tissue. The
splash breaks it up, and enables the antiseptic to make its
way down to the base of the ulcer. Probably, also, the continual "hammering" of the drops of liquid has a stimulat-
ing effect. At any rate, the ulcer gets cleansed in the course
of a few days; it assumes a good, red colour, and shows a
tendency to heal which we never could show to follow
with any other method.

If it is a very large and rapidly extending ulcer, it is
exposed to the drops both morning and evening; we also
make the solution strong, taking a gramme of oxycyanide
of mercury to three, or even to two, litres of water (3⅜ or
2¼ quarts).

What is put upon the ulcer for the bandaging between
the washings is comparatively unimportant. We generally
mix for it equal quantities of iodoform, dermatol, and salol.

Even when the ulcer is beginning to granulate, the drop-
ping is continued steadily, but with weaker and weaker
solution, so as to avoid any injury to the newly formed
tissue; we end with 1 gramme to 10 or 12 litres of water.

When the ulcer is perfectly clean we try, if it is a very

large one, to hasten the growth of the new skin by skin-grafting, and if this is successful the time wanted for the healing is shortened by at least a third.

But this treatment by falling drops gives good results with other kinds of ulcers too, many of them responding well to a solution of half a gramme of sulphate of copper in a litre of water. And it makes possible the use with any kind of ulcer of any desired disinfectant in a solution of any desired strength.

Extraordinarily useful in combating the many varieties of ulcer is a new disinfectant, a Swiss speciality called Breosan, which we usually apply in the form of a salve. Its success with the most varied kinds of ulcer is especially surprising when it is used on quite recent ones. We use hardly any other remedy than this for the so-called craw-craws from which Europeans suffer, and the origin of which is still obscure, although bacteriologically we frequently find staphylococci in pure culture.

I have tested Breosan on myself. Previously, every scratch I got on one of my feet turned into an ulcer, which gave me trouble for weeks. If on the new site I knocked my foot against a beam, or if it got chafed by my shoe, I knew that it meant an ulcer. But since beginning to treat every foot abrasion with Breosan I have not had an ulcer on either foot. We have now made it a rule to give every European a tube of Breosan for his travelling drug-box, and have been thanked for it again and again. I believe that Breosan ointment is going to play a big part in tropical medicine.

We are caused great anxiety by the cases, happily not numerous, in which the phagedenic ulcer infects deeply the surrounding tissues. As a rule the infection is confined to the ulcer itself, the difference between healthy and infected tissue being clearly marked. But if, as occasionally happens, the infection spreads along the subcutaneous fascial planes, or along the intermuscular septa, or along the tendon sheaths, or if it reaches the bone, the case becomes very serious. If this complication is noticed at once, an extensive incision into the tissues may be effective.

Otherwise hardly anything can be done; the infection spreads further and further, and death results. Anyone, therefore, who is treating such an ulcer, must be on the watch for any possible undermining of its edge. If that begins, an immediate intervention with the knife is called for.

There is at present no explanation of the facts that phagedenic ulcers form only on the lower leg, and that—in the Ogowe district at any rate—women are hardly ever attacked by them.

While treating the unhappily still numerous dysentery patients, Dr. Trensz makes a valuable discovery. It is well known that there are two sorts of dysentery, that caused by the unicellular amœbæ, and that which is traced back to dysentery bacteria. In the bacteriological laboratory which he has fitted up with the most primitive apparatus, Dr. Trensz undertakes the making of cultures from fæces of patients in which no amœbæ had been found. In these he proved the presence not of the dysentery bacilli but of vibrions closely akin to the cholera vibrions, and distinguished from them only by a different form of combination. It follows that what passed for bacillus dysentery is, in most cases, if his investigations prove correct, severe cholerine, produced by a paracholera vibrion.

Examination of the local water shows that this vibrion is endemic in the Ogowe district. Hence it is called the Vibrio Gabunensis, and Dr. Trensz has embodied his study of it in a good-sized scientific pamphlet.* So, perhaps, the dysentery which in Equatorial Africa always breaks out among the labourers on road- or railway-building is in a large number of the cases in which the presence of amœbæ cannot be proved, not bacillus dysentery but this cholerine. I long ago dealt with unexplained cases of dysentery by taking a hint from cholera-therapy and treating them with white argillaceous earth (bolus alba) dissolved in water. The results were favourable, and now Dr.

* This has since been published with the title : "Etude sur une diarrhée épidémique à vibrions observée au Gabon" (Strasbourg, 1928).

Trensz's researches explain why this treatment was effective. We have to deal with a complaint which is akin to cholera.

Cultivation of the vibrions in the laboratory enables Dr. Trensz to prepare a vaccine with which such cases of cholerine can be cured in two or three days.

In ordinary circumstances these water-borne cholerine bacteria are not dangerous to the natives. It is only when a diet of rice has destroyed the resisting power of the intestine that the infection is able to establish itself.

The fact that we doctors in Lambarene are now three in number allows us to work scientifically and make researches of great value for the treatment of our sick.

The doctor who works in the primeval forest single-handed is so fully occupied with the daily routine that he has neither time nor energy left for the investigation of puzzling cases. In every tropical hospital there should, therefore, be at least two doctors. Too small medical establishments are as unprofitable here as are too small mission stations.

Again, since there are several doctors, necessary journeys can be undertaken without the hospital work being affected. Almost every month we each spend some days travelling. At the beginning of June, Dr. Lauterburg undertakes a journey which is to last several weeks, made partly by water, partly by land, in the districts south of Lambarene. He is away an unexpectedly long time, and no news of him reaches us, so that we are beginning to get anxious, when one fine day we see him step out of a canoe, thin, indeed, but healthy and happy. He was the first doctor who had ever been seen in those parts, and he at once won the confidence of the natives, who knew of the Lambarene hospital by hearsay.

His report confirms us in our design of undertaking regularly long journeys like this, for there are numbers of sick far away from here who cannot travel to the hospital. The journey is too long, or the current of the river makes it too difficult, which is, indeed, the case for the districts lying to the south. Often, too, there is nobody to bring the sick to us. If, then, so many who need us cannot come to us, we must go to them.

If the hospital is to make available its full power for good, one of the doctors ought really to be continually going about with a well-supplied travelling dispensary, and the most necessary instruments, so that the necessary care may be given to those who can be treated where they live, and those who need hospital treatment can be brought back with him to Lambarene.

But for this plan there must always be three doctors, one for the ordinary work, one for surgery, and one for travelling. It is to be hoped that I shall be able to find the necessary men and means.

We are not compelled, fortunately, by the bacteriology to cut down the surgical work. Many and many a victim of hernia or elephantiasis gets relief from his suffering through the knife wielded by Dr. N'Tschinda-N'Tschinda. And the patients are, as a rule, very grateful. It may happen, indeed, that some man who has been operated upon is not prevented by gratitude from making off secretly in the night and taking with him as a souvenir the mosquito net lent him by the hospital. Such was the experience of Dr. N'Tschinda-N'Tschinda with a patient who had an enormous hernia, and gave the surgeon a great deal of trouble. However, the joy the surgeon felt at having given the needed relief prevented him from worrying over the ingratitude.

By way of precaution we require that the present made in return for the operation—usually bananas or other fruit, seedlings of bread-fruit trees, or of banana plants, or smoked fish—shall be brought by the relatives while the patient is still in the hospital. If he himself expresses an intention of bringing it after his discharge, there is reason to fear that he will be hindered from doing so through a change in his feelings or through circumstances. One of them, who really means his promise, wants to leave his second wife with me as a pledge, until he returns with the present. I decline his offer on the ground that the pledge will be difficult to look after.

With operations on elderly people, i.e., over fifty years of age, one must in Equatorial Africa be extraordinarily careful. They cannot endure being for so long on their backs. They often lose their appetite after an operation, and fall into a condition of weakness which may be very dangerous. Our experience has made us refuse to operate on elderly people, unless such drastic treatment is absolutely necessary to save their life.

Since April we have had with us Mlle Martha Lauterburg, the doctor's sister, as a nurse. She arrived at the same time as Hans Muggensturm. Our new, very experienced nurse takes over the service of the hospital, so that Mlle Kottmann can now devote herself entirely to the work of the plantation, the garden, and the new building site. A European, too, M. Ganne, has been helping us for months with the supervision of those who are felling the trees.

Mlle Emma Hausknecht manages the housekeeping, which is in truth the heaviest department of all our activities. She has a world of trouble with the cook to make him prepare the food with care and absolute cleanliness, not endangering our health by the use of unboiled water. Almost every day there are from twelve to fifteen Europeans to cook for. And the housekeeping is especially complicated because almost every day is washing-day, and there is always linen to be mended. The tidying of the rooms of the European patients also falls to Mlle Hausknecht. She has at her disposal, indeed, for helpers, the "boys" who have come with their sick masters, but what a job it is to keep these half-dozen boys in order!

Then there is still the care of the poultry and the goats. To avoid having to pay hard cash in Switzerland for all our milk, we are trying to rear a herd of goats. It is, indeed, only half a glass of milk a day that we get from each of these half-wild creatures, but we hope with time to improve the breed.

Mlle Hausknecht, the ever busy, seldom appears on the scene alone; Fifi, the baby chimpanzee, is always holding on to her apron. Fifi was brought to us a year ago when only a few days old, by the native hunter who had shot her mother. Mlle Hausknecht was at first terrified by the frightfully ugly creature, and would not touch it, but pity triumphed finally over all æsthetic inhibitions. Fifi has now got over her teething and can feed herself with a spoon without help. She had had for some time a play-mate in a somewhat older baby chimpanzee, which a European left with us when he returned to Europe, in order that he might be in good hands.

Europeans who are going home on leave often bring their dogs to us for the time, since they know that the animals will be well looked after. They never venture to entrust them to the natives, because the latter are quite capable of letting them die of hunger or thirst, or of treating them with thoughtless cruelty.

But while I am setting the piles I am allowed to discover that sympathy for the lower creatures can be aroused in even the most savage of the natives. Before the pile is lowered into the pit I look whether any ants, or toads, or other creatures have fallen into it, and if so, I take them out with my hands so that they may not be maimed by the pile, or crushed to death later by the earth and stones, and I explain why I do this to those who are standing by. Some smile in embarrassment; others pay no attention at all to what they have heard so often. But one day a real savage, who was working with me, was fetched to work in the plantation at cutting down the undergrowth. A toad being espied in it, his neighbour wanted to kill it with his bush-knife, but the first one seized his arm and unfolded to him and to a listening group the theory that the animals were, like ourselves, created by God, and that He will some day hold a great palaver with the men who torment or kill them. This savage was the very last on whom I should have expected my deeds and words to make any impression.

Our natives hear, with lively interest, of a European magician who is touring the west coast and giving performances in Cape Lopez. He is also giving personal interviews in which, in return for a fee, he reveals the future, and gives information about things which have been lost. Till now it has been only those natives who could read the newspapers who got to know about the luxuriant crop of superstition that flourishes among the whites, and many a time I have been questioned by native "intellectuals" about the advertisements of clairvoyant men and women who are at work in the big towns of Europe.

What is *our* position, i.e., the position of those who try to combat the superstition of the natives?

"So the white people, too, have magicians!" a native said to me. "Why have the missionaries and you, too, concealed that from us?"

The victorious advance into the colonies of European superstition is an event of far-reaching significance. It gives another tremendous blow to our spiritual authority, which has already been cruelly shaken by the war. The intelligent, reflecting natives are shocked by the discovery that there is superstition prevalent among us also, and at present heathen superstition is triumphing, thanks to the unexpected ally who has come to its support from across the sea.

And the professional European superstition is now beginning to exploit the negro. Natives in this neighbourhood, some of our orderlies among them, have had sent to them a prospectus from Roxroy Studios, 42, Emmastraat, Haag (Holland). They must send 50 francs, a lock of their hair, and the date of their birth, so that their horoscope can be cast, and they may receive the "Ki-Magi" talisman which corresponds to those signs of the zodiac which bear on their life. They must also say in their letter whether their talisman is to ensure success in business, good fortune in love, good health, or luck at cards. A talisman is offered which will bring success in all four, but it costs considerably more than the others.

Full of joy that they can obtain some of the advantages

of this mysterious wisdom, two of my orderlies come to me about it, and ask me to advance them part of their wages, so that the money demanded and the other requisites may go off by return of post. One of them regretfully admits that he does not know when he was born, but he hopes that the hair he sends will enable the astrologer to cast his horoscope. I am afraid that in spite of my explanation and my refusal of any advance, the prospectus was answered.

In the course of the summer Joseph leaves us, since the wages he gets from me are no longer sufficient. He has got married, and wants to spoil his wife—an energetic and prudent woman—with clothes from Europe, just as two or three native timber-merchants, who have made something out of their business, spoil their wives. But he cannot manage this on an orderly's wage, so he is going to devote himself to the timber-trade exclusively.

The departure of the man who was my only helper in the early days grieves me, but we remain good friends. If either of us can do a service for the other, he does it, and Joseph continues to style himself, "Dr. Schweitzer's first medical assistant." Fortunately, we have managed to attract several new black orderlies. The best of them is Bolinghi, and he is entrusted with the care of the surgical cases.

We find the painting of the completed buildings a heavy task. They must be colour-washed in some way to make them last longer, and we prepare the wash by adding size dissolved in warm water to a solution of well-sifted lime. Properly prepared and laid on, this colour-wash is in the tropics very nearly as serviceable as the much more expensive oil-paint. We use the latter only for those parts on which the rain beats during a thunderstorm.

We believe at first that we can train natives to do the colour-washing, but their chief contribution to the work is to ruin most skilfully the few brushes that we possess. If a primitive gets a brush into his hand the brush has in two days not a hair left. I do not know how they manage this, but so it is, and, as the colour-wash must also be laid on very carefully, there is nothing for it but to do the work ourselves. Doctors and nurses vie with each other in the practice of this unfamiliar art.

Mlle Kottmann is at work for many days on eighty sacks of rice which had got wetted during transport. First, space had to be made for the sacks to stand side by side instead of being piled one upon another. Then each one had to be cut where it was wet, the damp grains taken out, and then the sack sewn up again, after which the whole lot had to be carefully watched, to see that the contents of the sacks were not spoiling. A couple of handfuls of damp rice is enough in this hot climate to make the whole sackful mouldy.

We still have to keep something like two tons of rice permanently in store. The famine is diminishing, but only because sufficient rice is now coming from Europe. Had we to depend on locally produced food only, we should be in an uncomfortable position. Bananas and manioc are scarcely procurable. What we do manage to secure is only enough to feed a few patients who are absolutely unable to take the rice. Not till the new year comes, when the newly planted banana trees begin to bear, will the country be able once more to feed its inhabitants.

We burden ourselves with some extra work out of compassion for the palm trees, with which the site of our future home is crowded. The simplest plan would be to cut them all down. An oil-palm is valueless, there are so many of them. But we cannot find it in our heart to deliver them over to the axe just when, delivered from the creepers, they are beginning a new life. So we devote some of our leisure hours to digging up carefully those which are transplantable and setting them elsewhere, though it is heavy work. Oil-palms can be transplanted even when they are fifteen years old and are quite big.

That one should feel compassion for the animals my natives can understand. But that I should expect them to carry heavy palm trees about, so that they may live instead of being cut down, seems to them a perverted philosophy.

The hospital is never without Europeans as inmates. At the beginning of the year two European babies first saw the light under our roofs, one of the mothers having come a very long journey from the south along the sea coast in order to go through her confinement at Lambarene. For fourteen days she was carried by natives through forest and swamp, till she reached Cape Lopez, and was able to finish her journey in the river-steamer. For her return journey I discovered a motor-boat which was going as far as the Fernando Vaz Lagoon, which lies due south from Cape Lopez. In the Catholic mission station there she found hospitality till her husband could be summoned by messenger and could fetch her away with native carriers.

A few days later a European lady, seriously ill, arrives from the interior with her husband, an official, during the night and amid pouring rain. White patients are turned out, so that there may be a room free for them. And when she has been examined and provided for, there are the fifty natives to take in who were paddling the whole day in pouring rain without anything to eat. For they have come from the famine district. How we have to talk and scold to get the inmates to make room for them in the already overcrowded wards, and to give them some wood for their fires. Then by the light of lanterns the whole of the baggage has to be unloaded from the canoes, got under cover, and put in charge of watchmen. Finally, there is a liberal distribution of food, and it is past midnight when, tired and wet, we mount up to the doctor's house.

Since the lady is fit to travel and wants to get home, we take her the following evening to a small river-steamer which is going down to the coast. Dr. Nessmann leaves us by the same boat. The inmates escort their departing doctor by torchlight to the canoe which is to take him to the steamer's stopping-place, but the farewells there are hurried. We have scarcely put our dear helper and his baggage on board, when we have to be off at once, so as to get home before the burst of a thunderstorm that we see gathering.

Not long after this there arrives from the mission station

at Ovan, which is situated in the interior, 300 kilometres from Lambarene and in the famine district, Madame Rusillon, a missionary and missionary's widow, to recruit for a time in our hospital. She can hardly realise that she is living once more under normal conditions. As soon as ever we heard of the severity of the famine at the Ovan mission station, the missionaries here and we ourselves determined to send foodstuffs to it, and did so by the most varied methods of transport. I now learn that a small sack of 80 lb. of rice, which I entrusted to one of my European patients, was the first gift to arrive and just at the right time. What had been sent before that either arrived later or was lost *en route*.

In the dry season the bos'n of the crew of a canoe in which Dr. Trensz and Mlle Lauterburg were coming home just as night was falling, noticed with his sharp eyesight an unusual object on a sandbank near the hospital, and stopped the canoe. The object was a European who had got injured and was lying unconscious on the sand with his bundle. It turned out that he was coming from the interior, where he had been engaging negroes, and that his crew—newly engaged men from the interior—had found it simpler to put him out on the sandbank than to bring him to the hospital. The poor fellow recovered in the hospital so far that he could be sent to Europe some weeks later.

On the whole, Europeans decide much too late to come to the hospital; they often come when it is too late to help them. The responsibilities which they have to bear at the timber-sites, or in the distant factories, are so heavy that they decide to leave their post only under the pressure of the extremest necessity. To whom can they entrust the foodstuffs and wares for which they are responsible? Who will see that the trunks are rolled at the right time into the swamps and lakes and streams to catch the expected high water which will allow them to be piloted into the River Ogowe? To go into hospital, if there is no substitute to ruin. It is touching to see how in such cases Europeans take their place, means often nothing less than risk of in the forest mutually help each other, and undertake the duty of a neighbour, even if they live far apart and can only visit each other at the cost of a laborious journey.

Again, Europeans often leave the hospital too soon. A young man whom malaria and heart disease had left in a very bad way, insisted on returning to his post upstream because there was just then a good opportunity for travel. All entreaties and warnings were in vain. Three weeks later came the news that he was dead.

CHAPTER IX

1927. In the New Hospital

THIS year I can give to writing even less time than I could last year. The continual to and fro between the old and the new, and the work on the latter, fatigue me so much that I am incapable of work with the pen. I have no energy for anything beyond practising regularly on my piano with pedal attachment.

At the beginning of the year there are so many buildings finished that patients can be lodged in them, though there is still much to be done inside. But we must use the short, dry season for the removal, and further, we must empty the old buildings, so as to be able to use the materials in them for completing the new ones. In the primeval forest every old plank and every old beam is very valuable.

On January 21st the removal begins. Dr. Lauterburg, his sister, and Mlle Hausknecht look after the loading in the old hospital; Mlle Kottmann and Hans Muggensturm receive the patients and their belongings at the new. I myself am on the river the whole day towing the full canoes upstream, and bringing them back empty. Some white patients also come to our help with their motor-boats.

In the middle of it all a European arrives with his wife, who is expecting her confinement. Fortunately I have made allowance for such tricks of fate, and have had three rooms, with two beds in each, made ready in the house for the white patients. A quarter of an hour after their arrival the lady has settled in, and the removal can proceed.

In the evening I make the final journey and bring up the last patients, the mental ones among them, and the latter behave excellently. They have been told that in the new hospital they will live in cells with wooden floors, so they imagine that they are moving into a palace. In their old cells the floor was the damp earth.

I shall never forget the first evening in the new hospital. From every fireside and from every mosquito net they call to me : " This is a good hut, Doctor, a good hut ! "

For the first time since I came to Africa my patients are housed as human beings should be. How I have suffered during these years from having to pen them together in stifling, dark rooms ! Full of gratitude I look up to God who has allowed me to experience such a joy. With deep emotion, too, I thank the friends in Europe, in reliance upon whose help I could venture to move the hospital, and replace the bamboo huts with corrugated-iron wards.

On the day following the removal Dr. Trensz returns from a journey. He has no idea of what has been accomplished, and is intending to go farther downstream. It is only with hesitation that he acts on the news that is shouted to him from the bank, and lets his canoe be put in here.

From this time onward, Dr. Lauterburg, Dr. Trensz, and Mlle Lauterburg live in the house for the European patients in the new hospital. Hans Muggensturm had already taken up his quarters there in the autumn. The rest of us remain for a time in the old, doctor's house at the mission station, and the cooking is done at the old place. A canoe —which we call the " Restaurant Car "—conveys their food to those who now live in the new hospital.

Three days after the removal there sets in such a stream of European patients that we hardly know where to house them.

As soon as the dispensary has been emptied I start demolishing the buildings which are our property. Some of the buildings belong to the mission, and were only lent for our use. How carefully I have to watch to see that the natives do not injure the beams and the planks ! And what a labour it is to draw all the nails out of the wood, and to hammer them straight so that they can be used again !

The planks we thus obtain are used mostly for constructing the sleeping-berths, which, in the new wards, as in the old, are in two storeys, one above the other. This work Dr. Trensz superintends in his spare time, and he, practical man that he is, devises a method of construction which allows the bed-frames to be lifted down, so that they can be washed outside and left in the sun.

But before the last berth is finished he has to lay down his hammer and start for Europe, having been unable to keep himself free to stay for more than a year. On February 18th he leaves us, but we join him in hoping that at some future time he will be able to devote himself once more to the Lambarene hospital.

To replace him there arrives on March 23rd Dr. Ernst Mündler, from Switzerland, and accompanying him is an English lady, Mrs. C. E. B. Russell, who wants to help us in our labours. And she at once finds her proper sphere. She takes over the command of the people who are felling the forest and are working in the plantation, whereby Mlle Kottman is set free for other activities.

The natives soon make friends with their new feminine superintendent and obey her willingly. It is remarkable that the white woman has the greatest authority over primitive men.

An inseparable companion of Mrs. Russell is a little tame monkey, which I gave her as a present on her arrival. It goes with her every morning into the forest, and even if it does take a walk up in the trees, it always comes back loyally to its mistress.

As we have more work than we can manage to get through, we thankfully accept an offer of help for an indefinite time from a M. Karl Sutter, a Swiss, who has till now been in the timber-trade. He works with Mrs. Russell, because we want to get a big piece of forest cleared during the dry season.

Meanwhile we have fortunately got ready for use some of the rooms in our house on the hill; otherwise we should not know where to put the newcomers. And early in the summer the kitchen near it gets its roof on, so that cooking can be done up there. Before long, too, the fowl-house and the goat-kraal are ready, so that our livestock can be transferred.

While the doctors complete the internal arrangements

of the hospital, and Hans Muggensturm finishes off the dwelling-house on the hill, I set the piles for a house to contain five rooms, on the slope of the hill facing the hospital. It is for the doctors to live in some day. The other house on the hill is meant first of all for the nurses, but it contains also a room for sick European women, the common-room in which we dine, and store-rooms in addition. For in African houses there is neither loft nor cellar. Everything has to be stored in rooms.

I am also still at work building a big shed for the canoes and the boats.

Early in July the chief buildings are finished, though there is still much to do in the matter of internal arrangements.

The big pile-built village has quite a dignified look! And how much easier the work is now, for at last we have space enough, air enough, and light enough! How delightful we feel it, doctors and nurses all, to have our new rooms distinctly cooler than our old quarters were!

For the isolation of the dysentery cases wise precautions have been taken. Their rooms have no opening towards the hospital, and are approached on the side next the river. But from the river they are separated by a fence, so that they cannot pollute the water.

For the mental patients eight cells and a general sitting-room are in prospect. That I can provide for them so well I owe to an endowment which the congregation of the Guild House in Eccleston Square, London, has created for the sake of these poorest of the poor in my hospital in memory of a former member, Mr. Ambrose Pomeroy Cragg.

If the people concerned are patient sheep, and a number of them will go into one fold, the hospital can house some 250 patients with their attendants. And it is generally occupied by between 120 and 160.

While the two doctors are organising the routine of the new hospital, I get ready for my return home. It is three and a half years since I left Europe. Everything is now so well in order that I can leave the hospital to the care of my helpers.

The report that I am going to Europe has reached a mental patient, N'Tschambi by name, who is now allowed to go about in freedom. With tears in his eyes he comes to me and says: "Doctor, have you given orders that no one can send me away while you are in Europe?" "Certainly, N'Tschambi. No one can send you away without first having a great palaver with me." Deeply relieved, he presses my hands, and the tears stream down his cheeks. He had been brought to us some months before in chains, having in his mental darkness killed a woman. In the cell he gradually became quiet, and now he is so far restored that under a certain amount of supervision he can walk about, and even busy himself with a little work. He sharpens the axes, and goes with Mrs. Russell into the forest, where he helps with the tree-felling. As soon as it is noticed that he is getting restless, he is kept in his cell under observation. His continual fear is that he may be compelled to leave the hospital where he has been so well cared for, knowing well as he does, what sort of fate awaits him in his village. He is afraid, too, that while he is out of his mind he will be guilty of fresh misdeeds. How glad I am that I can offer to him and to others in the same misery a refuge for a long period!

On July 21st the hour strikes for my departure. Mlle Kottmann and Mlle Lauterburg are travelling with me. The former goes to recruit in Europe after three years' work here; the latter goes home to get married.

We have to wait several days at Cape Lopez for the steamer, which struck a sandbank in the Congo, and was got off with difficulty. But on the 29th we go on board. The boat pushes slowly out of the bay in bright sunshine, and with my two loyal helpers I gaze at the disappearing coast, hardly able to realise that I am no longer in the hospital. All the needs and all the work of the past three years sweep through my memory, and with deep emotion I think of the helpers of both sexes who have shared them with me, as well as of the friends and associations as whose deputy I was allowed to start this work of mercy. Joy at the success of it is not what I feel: rather I feel myself humbled, and ask myself how I earned the privilege of carrying on such a work, and in such a work attaining to success. And there breaks through, time and again, a feeling of pain that I must leave it for a time, and tear myself loose from Africa, which has become for me a second home.

It seems to me incomprehensible that I am leaving the natives for months. How fond of them one becomes, in spite of all the trouble they give one! How many beautiful traits of character we can discover in them, if we refuse to let the many and varied follies of the child of nature prevent us from looking for the man in him! How they disclose to us their real selves, if we have love and patience enough to understand them!

But the far-away green strip, behind which our thoughts would fain see Lambarene, is getting less and less distinct. Is it still there on the horizon? Or has it at last disappeared below the waves?

Ah, now there is no room for doubt. . . . There is nothing to be seen but water. So without a word we three press each other's hands and go down to stow away our belongings in our cabins, and so deaden a little the pain of parting.

THE END